BREAKING
TO BE ME

The Secret to Overcoming

Chronic Pain

by Jenny Harkleroad

Spotlight Publishing - Goodyear AZ

Breaking To Be Me – The Secret to Overcoming Chronic Pain
© Copyright Jenny Harkleroad 2019 First Edition
First Published in the USA by MBK Enterprises, LLC | Spotlight Publishing, Goodyear AZ
ISBN: 978-0-9980350-4-8 Paperback
ISBN: 978-0-9980350-5-5 Ebook
Library of Congress Cataloging-in-Publication Data:

Editor: Becky Norwood, Spotlight Publishing
Cover: Angie Analya
Photography by: Marcy Browe Photography, https://marcybrowe.com/
Interior Layout: weformat, www.vanzzsolutions.com

Disclaimer: ALL INFORMATION CONTAINED in this book and e-book is intended for your general knowledge only and is not a substitute for medical advice or treatment for specific medical conditions. I cannot and do not give you medical advice. If you have any specific questions about any medical matter, you should consult your doctor or a qualified professional healthcare provider. If you think you may be suffering from any medical condition you should seek immediate medical attention.
 - Jenny Harkleroad

Breaking To Be Me – The Secret to Overcoming Chronic Pain
Jenny Harkleroad
jenny@balancedyou.org
https://balancedyou.org

Introduction

I was unhappily racing down the freeway of life, full steam ahead, putting on a happy face for everyone to see, but I was breaking on the inside. I needed a shift, a major shift. How was I going to turn everything around? The task seemed daunting, even impossible. I felt like I had hit bottom physically and emotionally. That's when I physically jumped!

That jump BROKE MY BACK! Through my years of struggling to recover, what I learned was the secret to pain relief. I wish I could say it was a quick lesson learned, but the back break was only the beginning of a long journey of physical and emotional healing that eventually led me to my now joyful and pain free life.

This book is a love affair in many ways. Falling in love, out of love, and back eventually in love again with myself, my body, my emotions, my husband, and my purpose. Since you do not want your life's wake up call to be at the bottom of a rocky cliff, let's look at how we can create a gentle transition into your own pain free life.

This book is dedicated to my sweet husband who put up with me for decades when I was much less than lovable. Thank you for loving me while I healed!

To my wonderful children, who truly are angels on Earth. People ask me what we did to create such amazing kids and all I can say is they came to us like that. What a sweet blessing from above.

To my best friend Kelli, who was a lighthouse during my stormy years, and is a deeply trusted advisor, and always says what I need to hear, listens to me like no one else, and loves me unconditionally. Thank you Kelli!

To Dr. Warren Jacobs for helping me heal myself and find

and live my purpose. YOU helped me transform my life! I am forever indebted!

To my parents, siblings, extended family, friends and all my teachers along the way, I am truly blessed to know you. You are a big part of my story. I share my story, not to blame others or myself, but to share my perspective on why I struggled with chronic pain and how I overcame it. My hope and prayer is that others will find pain relief and hope from what they read in my story.

Praise be to God for always looking over me and helping me get back on track when I lost my way.

ENDORSEMENTS

"This book is a must read for anyone with a chronic health problem. It is the personal story of a truly remarkable, courageous woman who, in the process of healing herself, came to understand the body-mind connection. Jenny has grasped the TRUTH about chronic illness, something that despite my education as a medical doctor in a number of excellent universities, was training the doctors to treat symptoms instead of the cause that was behind the symptoms. In this excellent book, which I will recommend to many of my patients, she explains the process by which anyone with a chronic health problem has the opportunity to make not only a change in their health, but a new joy in their life - to live more fully - to be more alive - to improve relationships - to find greater satisfaction and meaning in life." - **Dr. Warren Jacobs, M.D.**

"Jenny's story in *Breaking To Be Me* is filled with hope, inspiration, and empowerment that our amazing bodies have the capacity to change. It is also a reminder that the traditional medical system frequently overlooks many of the intangible subconscious issues that can influence not only our pain, but our overall wellness." - **Melissa Cady, D.O.,** *The Challenge Doctor*

"I have had the privilege on numerous occasions to work with Jenny Harkleroad and her team. I have studied the mind, body, and alternative methods to overcome health issues, business blocks, and other challenges for years. Nothing compares to the brilliance of Jenny's work. She has taken issues, that I deemed impossible to change, and gotten results in one session. I am not about hype or miracles. I weigh heavily on results. Jenny and her team get results. I have worked with Jenny on eliminating my hot flashes

and it worked. I swear I didn't want to believe it was that simple, but it seemingly was. Jenny quickly and accurately connects the dots of your thinking to the problem. The minute I understood the connection, and after my reprogramming, I was able to put into action a plan to sustain my new belief and make it a new habit. I have referred Jenny and her team to everyone. She is the real deal."
- Jane M. Powers, JaneMPowers.com, *Speak with Confidence, Sell with Authority.*

"Breaking To Be Me" is one of those books that has the potential to completely change you. Inspiring and passionate, Jenny shares her story of breaking down completely only to rebuild her life simply by changing her perception. The stripping process is never fun to experience, but the benefits are easy to see in this fast paced, easy to read powerhouse of a book. **- Michael Brook, Speaker,** *Author of New Dimensions of Health, Coach and Professional Athlete*

"Jenny's story is incredible and so inspirational. How she maneuvered through the difficulty and pain and came out on the other side is one of belief, commitment, and strength on all levels. Her ability and desire to help others makes this world a better place is phenomenal. This book is a must read!" **- Wanda Allen,** *Follow-up Sales Strategies*

"Beautifully written! Jenny's story is so relatable. Her honesty and vulnerability helps us see our own struggles and gives hope that we can overcome our own stories of pain. If you don't believe your emotions cause physical pain or that you can reprogram your thoughts to live a full and happy life, you will believe it after reading this book!". **- Claudia Pratson,** *Evolved Leadership*

TABLE OF CONTENTS

CHAPTER 1

GROWING UP WRONG

Scan the QR Code above or go to this link to
see the video - https://youtu.be/9-Vg7t2Jyac

Jenny Through the Looking Glass, is a poem my mother posted on the side of my hospital bassinet when I was born. My parents were so excited to have me. They were married when they were 26 years old. My mom really wanted to have a baby and 11 months after the wedding, I was born.

I was a hard baby they said, colicky and never wanting to sleep. My defining feature was my glowing red hair which surprised both my parents when I was born. My dad's heritage is Irish, but for some reason, there were no redheads on either side of the family that they could recall. I was told one of my great grandmas use to say, "better dead than red". I'm sure she would have changed her

1

mind if she met me. From the photos I have, my young life looked happy, until I decided I didn't really need a mother. My mom made me do things I didn't want to do like take naps and obey. At two years old, I asked her if I could move out. My dad was not around much. He was a pharmacist when my parents got married and shortly after, decided to go to chiropractic school. My mom went back to work and I went to preschool.

My mom was in charge of me and I learned I better obey, or else! I didn't like the consequences if I didn't act, say, or do what my mom told me to. Sometimes, I'd stand up for myself. That never went well. I felt powerless, like something was wrong with me. No matter what I said or did, it always seemed wrong in my mom's eyes. As the years went on, I went from a happy bright-eyed kid to an actress. I would think, say, and do what I thought my mom wanted to hear. I ignored what I thought or wanted because it was never right. It was hard to live like this. How could I have been born so wrong, I wondered? I did my best to play the part, but inevitably I messed up. I walked around with a broken heart, knowing I was not okay. I put on a happy face and told everyone life was great because I didn't want anyone to think less of me.

In many ways my mom was a great mom. She loved me and treated me well more often than not. She drove me to all my school activities, worked hard around the house and garden, cooked lots of delicious and nutritious food, brought me to church, etc.

I also came into this life with a perfectionistic and do-gooder personality, so being told I was not okay was very painful. I felt emotionally wounded and believed something was wrong with me from a very young age. I felt that almost every time I opened my mouth, what came out was unacceptable. As time went on, every cross response she gave me was salt in my wound. Because of this, I was over sensitive to her responses as well. As early as elementary school I was always looking for a boyfriend; someone who would love me and tell me I was wonderful. I yearned for love and affection and to be told I was good enough as I was.

I found that "performing" well in school and music was pleasing to my mother and others. It gave me the positive encouragement I was yearning to hear. I obsessively focused all my time and attention there, practicing flute and studying every hour of everyday. Working at a local deli and teaching flute lessons helped pay for the used but beautiful BMW that I bought at 16 years old.

I had almost zero interest in school which made it really hard to get good grades, but I "forced" myself to get straight A's studying all hours of the night and receiving an academic scholarship to college.

I didn't have many friends. I was so uncomfortable with myself, I didn't know how to act around others. I needed to know the "rules" of how others wanted me to be, but unlike my mom, they didn't give me any. I knew I shouldn't be myself because I felt inherently bad or wrong. I really didn't know how to navigate friendship. I would tend to find one "safe" friend who I could be myself with and boy did I love them for it. That one friend would become my world, which also led to heartache because I was not always their world back. Actually, never was I their world back, but I wanted to be. I had to accept the love they were willing to give and that was hard.

I felt like a vortex, a black hole, with an unquenchable desire to be loved. If that friend would send me a sweet card or leave me a kind voice mail, I would obsess over it like it was the last bit of oxygen on earth, reading or listening to it incessantly. I say all this in hindsight and had no clue what was going on while I was in the thick of it. I knew I felt mad, bad, sad, in pain and very frustrated most of the time and pretended to be happy.

I was a natural born leader which I guess I could not hide because I was always asked to be in charge of everything. I was president of the National Honor Society in High School and drum major of my middle school and high school band. A drum major is the person who gives commands via whistle while marching in front of the band spinning a very large baton. No, a drum major is not a drummer, nor was I the majorette who typically wears a leotard, dancing and tossing a baton high in the air out near the color guard, A.K.A., flag team. I practiced so much with that large roped military baton that I literally wore a path in our front lawn while I marched back and forth.

In my senior senior year of high school I won 1st place at every drum major competition the whole year and my mom was so proud. I even saluted her at a parade and she still tells that story to this day. She wanted my love and respect but I felt she had not earned it because of the way she treated me. Sometimes I didn't give her much love back and I believe, that's why the salute meant so much to her.

Early in high school I played basketball, but didn't invite my parents much as I was not the star of the team and didn't want them to see me in any light but perfection. My self-esteem could not take any more hits. Not that I thought that they would say something negative, I just wanted positives or nothing. It was not surprising that I was not a great basketball player as I'd never played before. Not sure how I even made the team.

Oh, wait, I know how I made the team. I listened to everything the coach said and tried harder and pushed myself more than anyone else. Suicide drills, yes! I beat the whole team every time. Was I faster? Probably not, but I made it look like I was by pushing myself harder than anyone else. I wanted the praise and succeeded making the team.

I ran track, too. I was pretty good at doing sprints, hurdles, jumps and relays, but the coach pushed us really hard and you probably know by now, I didn't like getting pushed. I already did my best all the time. How can I give more than my best? One season of a tough track coach was enough for me and I didn't return the next season.

Being boy crazy continued. I met my future husband at age 14. I was at a church dance and he asked me to dance. I was praying he didn't ask my age when I found out he was 4 years older than me and happily he didn't! Yahoo! He told me he was leaving on a church mission for 2 years and asked for my mailing address and said he'd write me from Brazil. He left when I was 15 and we wrote on and off while I continued to chase any guy I could catch. I continued to write on and off to Dusty the missionary.

At one point, I moved with my family and he got transferred in Brazil. We no longer had each other's addresses. I remember looking up his home phone number in the white pages. Older folks will know what that is, and calling his house. His mom answered and with my heart pounding, I got his current mailing address again. We kept writing on and off. As the end of his mission got closer, I started getting excited. I was now 17 and about to be a senior in high school. He was 21 and coming home soon to head back to the local junior college he had been attending before he left on his mission. We lived about 45 minutes from each other. I was hoping he'd still be interested in me.

The week he was coming home I was so excited I could hardly stand it. I knew he was arriving on Saturday and I was waiting by the phone. My mom suggested I stop waiting by the phone and watch a movie to get my mind off of him. We chose the movie Pure Country. The movie opens with crowds of people chanting "Dusty, Dusty, Dusty!" Was this some kind of joke? Turns out the movie was a love story between a redhead and a cowboy named Dusty. This movie did not help me get my mind off MY Dusty!

The days continued on and Dusty didn't call me! My mom said college was starting in less than a week and he was probably trying to get settled moving back home from Brazil, registering for college and applying for jobs. None of her reasoning helped. Why wasn't he calling me? A week had gone by and I could not take it. I called him! *Ring, Ring,* "Hello?" He answered.

"Hi. Is this Dusty?"

"Yes."

"Hi this is Jenny."

"Jenny who?"

I'd like to say my heart sank, but it was more like my blood boiled! How could he say that?! We had been writing for two years! Dang, I wasted a lot of time and stationary on this guy! What a jerk!

"Jenny Hefferon."

"Oh, hi."

"Do you have your homecoming talk at church tomorrow?"

"Yes."

"Would you like me to come?"

"If you want to."

"Ok, maybe I'll see you tomorrow."

"Bye."

What the heck just happened? He doesn't remember me and he does not care if I come to his homecoming talk. There is no way I'm going! I can't believe this guy!

After that phone call, I had plans to go to dinner with a friend that night but now I didn't feel like going out at all! I went to her house and told her the whole story and explained that I did not feel like going out anymore. She kept telling me we'd have fun and that I should just go! I reluctantly gave in after quite a bit of coaxing!

We arrived at Acapulco Mexican Restaurant in Escondido, California and walked in. The hostess said, "oh that guy is here," while looking at my friend. I thought great, now my friend invited a boyfriend of hers to join us for dinner. Can my day really get any worse?

Again, the hostess repeats, "that guy's here and he's been waiting a long time."

I say, "what guy?"

My friend tells the hostess who happens to be a girl from our high school to "shut up!"

I say, "what is going on?"

My friend says "nothing."

The hostess says, "no, he's here!"

My friend gives her a look like she's going to kill her!

Then the hostess says, "wait, is this a surprise for him?"

My friend says, "No, it's a surprise for Jenny."

Now I'm really confused. "A surprise for me?"

Dusty walks in the door. In typical missionary fashion he shakes my friend's hand and then says to me, "you're Jenny Who?"

"Oh my gosh! I was hating you for the last few hours!" He laughed.

"You totally threw me off guard when you called. I was getting ready to drive up here for this surprise date your friend set up for us. When you called, I just wanted to get off the phone so I didn't ruin the surprise."

"I guess I don't hate you then," I joked.

"Shall we get some dinner" he asked.

"Yes!"

My friend, Dusty and I enjoyed dinner. At one point my friend saw some other friends and left us alone to chat. Dusty and I were immediately hitting it off and I was infatuated. I loved listening to his adventures and telling him what I'd been up to. I'm sure we ate, but I don't even remember that part. I do remember that he paid for dinner for the three of us, so sweet, and then we headed to the parking lot.

Dusty loved country music, but I was not much of a fan. Things had changed while he was gone. I had moved to a town where the only music with radio station reception was a country music station. Country music grew on me and I had learned some line dancing. Dusty said he had not heard country music in two years and didn't know if he was still a fan. We turned on the car radio while my friend and I lined danced in the parking lot of the restaurant. Dusty stared at me grinning. I could feel the sparks flying. When we finished dancing he again shook our hands in missionary fashion, which meant, no hugging girls. He was still not quite over that rule, and wished us a good night.

The next morning, my mom and I went to his homecoming talk at church. Dusty grew up being very close with his scoutmaster's family. Turns out the wife of his scoutmaster has big red wavy hair like mine. The scoutmaster's little boy walked into church, saw me from the back, thought I was his mom and came and sat next to me. When he looked up at me, he was quite surprised when he realized I was not his mom. Dusty said that was a good sign to him that I was "the one."

The location my mom and I sat was a bit hard to see Dusty because the podium was blocking our view of each other. Every few minutes, we'd see Dusty lean out from around the podium to get a good look at me. It was cracking my mom and I up. Adorable. Dusty gave a great talk and after church we invited him to our house for dinner. He came over and I showed him around our house. After being a missionary with strict rules not to be alone with girls, he was so awkward and uncomfortable around me. He could not wait for the house tour to be over so we could get back to a room full of people. I thought his shyness was cute and understandable.

We were both very busy with school and work during the week so we'd see each other on the weekends. His shyness around me was quickly getting old. I wanted a kiss. A few weeks after we started dating he told me that he really thought I was the right girl for him and that he wanted to marry me. I told him I was feeling the same way, but if he married me, he'd have to touch me. He said he eventually would, but it was still uncomfortable from all those strict missionary rules he'd been following.

We had so many fun dates. The entire high school asked me every Monday if he had kissed me. It was getting frustrating and embarrassing to say no! I asked Dusty if he wanted to go country dancing. I thought if he got a chance to touch me while dancing it might help him get more comfortable with the physical part of our relationship. While dancing he said, "want to go outside?" He took me by the hand and led me outside to the side of the building. "I've got something for you that I know you've been waiting now a long time for," he said. My heart was racing, finally the kiss was coming! He leaned in, handed me a hand full of chocolate kisses, led me by the hand back into the building and onto the dance floor. NOOOOOOOO! I can't face my friends on Monday! I wanted a kiss so bad! I didn't think this little stunt was funny at all! He sure thought it was!

We danced and enjoyed our night. When we got back to my house to say goodnight I decided if he didn't kiss me, I was going to kiss him! He did kiss me, and I kissed him back! Many times. Fireworks!!! Hooray!

Dusty asked me to my senior prom and we had so much fun dancing the night away. We left the dance and went to the beach. As we were watching the waves roll in under the moonlight Dusty asked me to marry him. I asked, "where is the ring?" He said, "well, I was not planning to ask you, so I didn't bring a ring." In my no nonsense fashion I told him I'd love to marry him, as soon as he got a ring and asked me properly, I'd say "yes"! Before long, he asked me to marry him the right way, and I said "yes"! We were head over heels infatuated! I was still 17 years old! Surprisingly, my parents were okay with it. I think my mom had had enough dealing with me and was ready to pass me off. Plus, she really liked him.

She also said I always had a mind of my own and knew what I wanted, so she was not going to try to stop me. I had an academic scholarship to college at BYU on their Hawaii campus, so I decided I'd go for a year and then come home and get married.

Leaving Dusty to go to college was hard. I cried all the way to Hawaii. The poor lady in the seat next to me trying to comfort me. After being away at school for about a week, all I wanted was to be home with Dusty. I called from the school pay phone and asked how he felt about me coming home after one semester, instead of a year, and getting married right after Christmas. He happily agreed, and so it was.

Wedding planning was brutal with my mom who wanted the wedding and reception to go her way and me who wanted it to go my way. I was also in a lot of trouble with her because of my apparent lack of appreciation for the parts of the reception my parents were paying for. I really appreciated them but her perception was that I did not. The battles raged on between my mom and I. We got to the wedding day without a plan for the details of the reception because I would not agree to her ideas and she would not listen to mine. The wedding was pretty much set by the church, so we only needed to make decisions regarding the reception. Luckily, an older sister of one of my friends, stepped in at the reception as a pseudo wedding planner and ran our reception for us while we followed as she directed. Thank you Sheila for saving the day!

The wedding and reception were beautiful. The honeymoon was even better! When we got home, we lived in a little 450 square foot apartment close to the local junior college and we both started attending school. I gave up my full academic scholarship at BYU-Hawaii. I was happy to do it to be with Dusty.

Soon after our wedding, I was introduced to a multi-level

marketing company and I bought in, hook line and sinker. I thought I was going to be rich, so I quit college, since I hated it anyway, and didn't know what I wanted to be, besides rich. I started working on building this network marketing business along with working for a bank. Because of my confidence, I asked the bank if I could have a desk job. I didn't want to be a teller. Amazingly, they gave me this job. It was pretty scary as I was 18 and hardly knew anything about banking, except while growing up, I had a savings account my mom controlled. I was pretty clueless about banking, barely knowing the difference between a debit and a credit. There was no training for my job other than learning as I went along. I remember having butterflies in my stomach as I'd go to work because of my lack of banking knowledge.

Luckily, the other employees at the bank were kind and helped me a ton since I asked a million questions. A customer would walk into the bank and say to me, "Hello, I'd like to make a deposit to my IRA." "Sure, one moment please," I'd respond thinking to myself, what the heck is an IRA?

Before long, I had the keys to the bank and enjoyed being the first one there in the morning to open and sometimes to lock up at night as well. I learned a lot about banking and enjoyed my time there.

Dusty was working full time and going to college full time, so I didn't see him much. When he was home, he was either studying or "relaxing" in front of computer games. I felt lonely a lot. Dusty and I started getting into arguments about my multi-level marketing business venture, as there were quite a few expenses involved. He thought the whole thing was a scam and I thought it was our ticket to riches. I tried to get him to see the business how I saw it, and he tried to get me to see it how he saw it. After a while, we just stopped talking about it. He'd be mad that I'd be spending money to go to out of the area business rallies. I'd do it anyway because I was tired of being told what I could and could not do from my growing up years.

About a year after we got married, I started having dreams. Dreams that a little girl wanted to join our family. The last thing on my mind was having a baby. I wanted to get rich, not have a baby. I tried to ignore this repeating dream, but it just kept getting louder. At one point this night time dream became a daytime dream, too. This little girl was haunting me. One time when I was praying with a group at church, I felt her come up next to me and grab my hand. That was crazy and scary! OKAY, okay, okay, if you need to be born so bad, I will have you I told her! I told Dusty about this and we decided to get pregnant in order for the haunting to stop.

At somewhere around 4 weeks pregnant I got the flu or so I thought. Problem was, this flu would not go away. Morning sickness had hit. How had I never heard of this before? I was throwing up all day and all night. I quit my job, lost 20 pounds, and slept and threw up for 3 months until one day, as fast as it came on, it was gone, and I went back to work.

About 5 months before Bekah was born, we bought our first house in North San Diego County. I was only 20 and Dusty 24. We were excited that we were already buying our first home. It was a major fixer upper, and we spent our weekends working on the house. The slab was cracked so bad that there were weeds growing in the living room and kitchen. Worse than that were the fleas and cockroaches. Gross! We quickly got the house fixed up and cleaned.

When Bekah was born, I quit my job as I wanted to stay home with her. Dusty didn't know how he'd pay for the house without my income, but before we knew it, he found a job paying twice what his previous job paid. Go, Dusty!

Being home with Bekah was quite an adjustment. I was used to being busy. I'm somewhat of a workaholic. Even as a kid I was always asking my mom for a job I could do and loved earning money. I love to accomplish tasks and hated wasting time. I was now home 24/7 with our baby. I could not bear the thought of having someone else take care of her, but the new very slow life proved quite challenging. I really didn't have any hobbies as my hobby was working. We had no TV as we could not afford one. I didn't like to read. These were the days before cell phones or internet.

Bekah was a very colicky baby and I think I cried as much as she did not knowing what to do with my crying baby. I was also bored, lonely, and sleep deprived. Dusty was still in school full time and working full time. His computer gaming past-time was turning into more of an addiction. This was the first time I remember wanting to leave my marriage. I didn't even feel like he cared about me anymore. My belief system taught me that I was to stay married, for better or for worse. Suck it up is what I thought I had to do. I was a good actress. I could play the part. I worked hard at getting people to be impressed with me. I couldn't get divorced. What would everyone think about me? I'm not moving back home with my mom, dad, younger siblings, and a baby. I'm not putting this sweet baby in daycare and going to work. I felt stuck and I did what some stuck people do when they don't know what to do. I stayed put.

While Dusty and I were dating I noticed how much he loved kids. Kids always wanted to talk, hang out, and wrestle with him. My little brother who is 10 years younger than me loved Dusty and looked up to him. Dusty built him a treehouse and they had a lot of fun together. I loved this quality in Dusty and knew he'd be a great dad. The one thing I didn't know was that he didn't like babies! I found this out the hard way when I'd ask him to help me with our daughter. He'd hold her for a few minutes, but that was about his limit. Bekah was pretty much my job, as was the house cleaning, bill paying, and laundry.

Dusty seemed to be detaching from me and our little family. The more I needed him, the more unavailable he was. I was trying to get him to make me happy by participating. I thought that is how it worked. When he wouldn't cooperate with my wishes, I'd resort to yelling, crying, silent treatment, even hitting him which would make him laugh because he's a big dude and I'm a small gal. The laughing just made me more furious. When I'd act like this, he'd leave and not come home for a while, even overnight. I'd apologize of course and try to "act" like I was supposed to. I'd be thinking, if he'd just be more involved, then I'd be happy. It's his fault I'm acting like this. I'm just reacting to how he is acting. I took zero blame for our troubles.

Our bedroom situation was not much better. I didn't understand how to find pleasure, so I'd blame him for not doing it right. Of course, that would cause him to want to play video games instead of taking me to bed which "made me" feel sad, frustrated and lonely. Is this really how life is going to be? I'm 21 years old and this is what I get to endure from here on out? I tried to ignore how I felt. My business venture gave me something to think about other than my loneliness and frustration.

Bekah grew out of her colic and started growing up a bit. Motherhood became much more pleasurable. We'd go to parks, libraries, the beach, etc. We were having a lot of fun together. She was my little buddy.

Since moving away from home, my mom and I were getting along better. My mom loved Bekah and I loved that she wanted to babysit, so I could spend time building my network marketing business. Bekah loved Grandma and they'd have a lot of fun together.

When Bekah was two years old, I wanted to have another baby. Dusty agreed and we got pregnant again. This pregnancy was much easier, as was labor and Jessica was an easy baby. Bekah was a big helper and the three of us enjoyed life together.

My relationship with Dusty was pretty much the same. We had some good times, but I was usually annoyed about something or other. He was never around, didn't help with the house or kids, and was not very interested in me.

I was still spending time and money on my network marketing business which he saw going nowhere. I didn't know how to make things better with us. I learned to be a blamer from my youth, so that's what I did. I thought if he would change, then things would be better with us. I dreamed of leaving him. Finding a guy who could "make" me happy. When things would get really bad between us, we'd see a counselor. I'd complain that Dusty was not involved or engaged. The counselor would tell him to get involved and engaged. He would for a short time until it would fade back into the way it used to be. This cycle repeated and repeated for years and then decades.

The arguing got really intense about my networking business and Dusty gave me an ultimatum. If I was not at a certain level of success by a certain date, then I had to give it up. This did not go over well, but I worked as hard as I could to get there. I do believe in working hard, but I also believe if it's meant to be it will be. This was clearly not meant to be as I worked myself silly for seven years and basically got nowhere.

I learned a lot along the way, reading a lot of business and success books, but for some reason I just could not find the right people to grow my network marketing business team. I followed the business program exactly like I should, I just didn't find success. The ultimatum date came, and I quit as I had not achieved my goal. Dusty was happy, but I was mad at him. Of course, I made it his fault. I thought the reason the business didn't work was because he wasn't helping me with it and instead was always talking down about it, saying that multilevel marketing is a scam.

I looked for other work from home businesses because I was always looking to make money and have something productive to do with myself when the kids didn't need me. I did some phone sales jobs and sold office supplies on eBay.

One day my dad asked if I'd listen to some marketing tapes that he had purchased. He wanted my advice on applying these marketing techniques to growing his Chiropractic business. At the same time, Dusty had recommended I get a real estate license so we could invest in properties and find deals before they hit the market.

When I listened to these business marketing tapes for my dad, I saw that I could apply these techniques to real estate and maybe do more, much more, than invest in our own properties. I signed up for an online real estate school and started studying. By then I was pregnant with baby number three, sweet Ashley, and got my real estate license two months before she was born.

I started selling real estate immediately. I remember being out showing houses only a week after Ashley was born. There were many church ladies who I paid over the years to watch the kids for me while I built my real estate business. The market was great when I got into real estate and my second year, I made $250,000 in commission. This drastically changed our lives. We built a 5 bedroom plus office custom home on 3 acres in a lovely part of town in North San Diego County. We went on fancy vacations, bought new cars, built other homes for investment properties and I was still in my 20's. Life looked pretty good from the outside. On the inside, all the same problems still existed. I worked so hard that I almost covered up the pain I was dealing with both mentally, physically, and emotionally.

When a real estate sale would fall through, or the market would slow down, money stress would set in from all our expenses. All the physical, emotional and marriage pain would flair up to an unbearable level. Again, I'd blame Dusty. If he'd help with the kids more, help around the house more, or want to spend time with me, then I'd be happy.

As the real estate market continued to crash around 2008, I worked harder and harder to keep it all up. We started selling off the rental properties we had in order to keep our heads above water. These were stressful times. I didn't understand how Dusty could work so hard for so little pay compared to the big real estate money I was making. Why did I have to pay the bills? Why wasn't he moving up faster? If he would just...you know the story.

Even with all this craziness, Dusty wanted a son! He bugged me about it incessantly. One day while at our church Temple, God told me to have another baby. Like a bratty teenager I stomped my feet and griped, FINE! I told Dusty and he was excited. We got our boy. Joshua was born. Dusty still did not "do" babies. All the work pressure, three other kids and a baby he didn't want to help with, was on me. I was starting to crumble as was the real estate market. I was starting to no longer enjoy real estate. It was a necessary evil to keep up the "success" image I had created for us. Top producer medals around my neck, large commission checks, companies offering me incentives if they could use my name to promote their product, as well as employees, including including a team of buyer's agents. It was too much.

As I learned from my youth, "put on a happy face," and I did. I always felt mad, bad, sad, sick, in pain and stressed out on the inside, but I told everyone, besides Dusty, that life was great! I wanted to feel great, but I definitely did not. During real estate office meetings,

I'd daydream about running away. I also thought about changing careers, but what work could I do from home so I could be with the kids and make big money with no college degree or expertise? I couldn't think of anything so I kept my nose to the grindstone.

Our marriage struggles continued. The unhappier I was, and the more blame I gave Dusty, the more distant he was. He became buddies with our oldest daughter and they were always going off having fun together. I was very jealous and didn't understand why he wanted to be with her instead of me. At year 15 of marriage, I told him I could not take it anymore and threatened divorce. Surprisingly, he still wanted me, got very depressed and more distant. We went to therapy and the cycle continued. The therapist told him to be more involved with me and the kids, the chores etc. He'd be on his best behavior and then he'd start to slide back into his ways.

I took his behaviors as a sign that I was not worthy, valuable or loved. I already came into the marriage feeling this way, so this was salt to my wound. I can't even begin to describe how bad I felt in our marriage. It was so painful for me. I'd continue to get my feelings hurt and wanted to leave again. This was a terrible cycle that I could not seem to break.

One day while taking a shower, I did break. I had a nervous breakdown. I thought I was having a heart attack. I yelled for Dusty. He came, saw me sobbing in the shower, holding my chest and losing my mind. He asked what he could do. I didn't know. I could not even talk. He left. I thought he was going for help. To call 911 maybe. No help came. When I finally got over it, I went looking for him and found him sleeping in a downstairs bedroom. I woke him up saying, "I almost died." He said he didn't think there was anything he could do and he was tired, so he went to bed. Guess what? I was mad again. Something has to give, I can't go on like this I thought. Well something did give, something major.

Chapter 2

The Day Everything Changed

Scan the QR code above for follow this link to view my video. https://youtu.be/BjxFjmRNuss

August 10, 2013, I was standing on a rocky ledge on the side of a mountain in San Diego. I'd been camping and hiking with family and friends and feeling a little prideful that this easy hike we went on was exhausting some of the people around me. My husband and I got separated from our group and found ourselves standing on a rock, deciding how to get down. My husband said, "If I was young and in shape I'd jump from here." Well, my pride got the better of me and I jumped! Really, it did not seem that far. They say it was only 9-10 feet, but I guess that when you land wrong on a rock 9-10 feet down, well, it was enough to hurt me very badly. While I was in the air, I realized I was probably going to land pretty hard and was worried about my knees. I decided to bend my knees to try to make a softer landing. While that may have been good for my knees, it was not so good for other parts of me. I landed on my feet, but because my knees were so bent, I slammed my butt and feet onto the rock at the same time. I immediately heard and felt a crunch in my back and started yelling in pain.

Dusty told me to walk it off, but this was not walkable! Friends were hiking down the mountain. They found us and started trying to help. They wanted to figure out if they could get me up from off the rock I landed on and off the mountain. They tried to move me, but I would not let them because the pain was too much to bear. They ran back to camp and brought back a chair, thinking they could carry me out. No way could they even get me into that chair. It was way too painful. Not only that, if there was any way they could get me back to camp, then what would they do with me? We were about 3-4 miles of bumpy dirt road away from a smooth surface and quite far from a hospital. We had no cell service, but turns out that 911 works even with no service. That was the best news of the day!

The not so good news was that emergency services would not send a life flight immediately since I was not dying. They told us they would send in a ground crew to assess my situation. Eventually I could see the ground crew hiking in their yellow jackets through the forest below. I thought they'd never get to me as they appeared to be so far away and they were walking! The pain was getting worse as time passed as the adrenaline wore off and I started yelling in pain. Vultures started circling me, no joke!

The emergency ground crew finally did get to me and decided I did need life flight. I was happy yet annoyed with that determination. We had told them I needed life flight an hour ago! The ground crew started asking me questions to gauge my mental state. What do you like to do for fun? Do you have kids? What are their ages? I was half crying and half arguing with them, telling them I was not in the mood for their questions and I would be just fine, just get me off the mountain. They told me they were going to roll me over, put a neck brace on me and strap me to a board. Then life flight could zip line me up because we were on a mountain side and life flight could not land. A doctor zip lined down to me from the hovering helicopter and he and the life flight crew rolled me over and taping me down.

I screamed even louder as they were moving me into an even more painful position and taped me down. I have this thing about being held down. I hate it and lose my mind, which is what started to happen! I was thrashing and yelling and trying to break free! Of course, that was not the smartest idea while I was dangling from the zip line of a helicopter. As the zip line was pulling me up, I remember the noon day sun shining so brightly that I could not possibly open my eyes. As I was moving through midair in a dangling basket and yelling in pain, I remembered I had my two favorite things in my pocket, gum and Chapstick. I stopped screaming and smiled for a split second, then went back to screaming.

I did not even realize at the time, but later saw in photos, that the doctor who had zip lined down to help me was now attached to me as we were pulled back up to the helicopter. The doctor must have thought I was crazy during the gum and Chapstick memory moment. When they got me in the helicopter, they shot me with a few rounds of morphine and I stopped thrashing around and mellowed out.

At the hospital, after MRI imaging, doctors told me that my back was broken. They said it would be 6 weeks until I could go back to normal life. I should have been in a place of gratitude that I was not paralyzed but my big worry was missing exercise and gaining weight. I was not sure I'd survive 24 hours without exercise. I was supposed to be at an Ashtanga Yoga class that night with my bestie, Kelli. Exercise had become a great outlet for my internal pain. I could hardly move with a broken back so that helped to keep me down. It didn't however, keep the tears from pouring out. What does a Type A person with a very busy life do when bed rest is suddenly non-negotiable? Cry, delete all my yoga and gym classes off my phone schedule, find lots of rides for my four kids to their four different schools and activities, get others to help cover my church, volunteer, and work commitments, journal, read, and WAIT.

I thought the 6 weeks would never end, but when they did, I was very aware that my body was not ready for exercise. I wanted to move. I was dying to move! I went to the gym and joined the water aerobics class. It was nice to get out, fun to move, a little odd exercising with grandparents in the pool, and cold, too cold!

After about a month of cold water aerobics, I felt that I could carefully go back to yoga. Boy was that a happy day! Instead of tackling every challenge like I used to, I had to baby every move. Prior to breaking my back, I had a hip injury from doing a cool yoga trick that I was not flexible enough to do. Even though I'd been on bed rest for my back for 6 weeks, that hip didn't feel any better, maybe worse. I wondered how my hip could hurt so much. I did my best to ignore the hip pain. Bad idea! By December 2013, I was starting to limp a bit when I walked because of the left hip pain, and then I started missing yoga classes. Noooooooooooo!

Another month passed, and I had to stop exercising completely due to hip pain. I could not even walk in the pool as my hip hurt so much. The doctor ordered an MRI of my hip and lower back (yes, my back was still hurting too) to see what they could find. Unfortunately, they found a black circle in my femur bone that sent us on a wild goose chase trying to figure out what it was. First, I was sent to an orthopedic surgeon. He said I was missing part of my femur bone. He said he could do surgery and put screws into my hip to keep it from breaking apart, but he really didn't know for sure what was going on. The doctor then ordered a bone scan to rule out cancer. Another chain of unfortunate events began.

Apparently, I'm allergic to Bone Scan I.V. contrast. This is not the kind of allergy where your heart stops and the doctors attempt to resuscitate you or sticks you with an EpiPen®. This was an after the bone scan, I'm-not-feeling-well type of allergy. The next day my arms and legs started to tingle. The next day, I couldn't move my legs and went back to the doctor in a wheelchair. The doctor said it might be multiple sclerosis or Guillain–Barré syndrome. Off to the neurologist I went, and then back to the lab for an MRI of the brain to rule out MS. The neurologist stuck me with a safety pin all over my body. Really, there is no higher-tech tool to check my sensitivity than a safety pin!?! "No MS," they said.

Then my arms stopped working. I was slowly becoming paralyzed. I read about Guillain–Barré syndrome, and apparently your body shuts down until your heart and lungs just stop. Later that afternoon, I was lying in bed, and could hear the kids playing downstairs. I was losing the ability to speak and really thought that I was going to die. I decided to call Dusty. My cell phone was on the bed right next to me. I couldn't move; I couldn't reach my phone. I struggled and finally got to where I could push the speed dial button. He answered. I tried to speak, and I couldn't. He told me he was almost home even though I was not speaking.

Before I knew it, he was standing by my bed with my parents, who happened to be in the neighborhood too. I heard them saying they were going to call 911. I whispered a faint "no." They took my pulse, rubbed my head, and talked to me. Then they said that I needed to go to the hospital. Again, I forced out an almost silent "no." For some reason, they listened to me and stayed by my side, taking my pulse, blood pressure (my chiropractor dad happened to have a blood pressure cuff with him) and watching me breathe. Within a few hours, the feeling started coming back into my body and I "woke up." I was able to move a bit and speak. It was as if the allergic reaction had hit its peak and I was on the recovering side of the reaction.

The next morning a lovely friend from church, who is one of those people that is so healthy that you wonder if it's healthy to be that healthy, was sitting on my bed with a basket of health remedies to cure me of this apparent reaction. It was a mix of green powders, herbs, vitamins, lemons, etc. She then spoke to me about health and the body's ability to heal. She cried, and read me our church health code. I was surprised how much health touched her. She inspired my interest, desire, and wonder about health, and put me on a detox that second.

The following week I went to the UCSD Cancer Center to

review my bone scan and hip issues. The doctor said they didn't think the dark circle in my hip bone was cancer, but they thought my hip was about to break if I put any pressure on it. If it broke, I would need a hip replacement, and they considered admitting me right then to do a hip replacement. They took another x-ray and decided to hold off on the immediate hip replacement. They ordered another MRI and handed me a pair of crutches. How does a mom of four, realtor, Relief Society President (I ran the women's organization for our church congregation, with about 275 in our group), and helping with other local charities live her life on crutches? Not to mention all the other drama I had recently been through from breaking my back?

I went to the fridge to get some food. How do you open the fridge without letting go of the crutches? How do you do anything with your hands while holding crutches? I strategically placed rolling desk chairs around my house so I could scooch with my good right leg to the fridge, then to the counter, over to the blender to make my green detox drinks, then from the washer to the dryer, and so on. Later that day, a friend brought a wheelchair and that worked even better. Those swivel wheels on that wheelchair were awesome. I was back in business!

I went back to the cancer center to review my MRI, and the doctor said, "Your left hip ligament is torn really badly. I mean really bad, like you were in a horrific car accident. Your hip was pulled out of the socket very hard during your back breaking landing and then snapped back. It's extremely stretched out and needs four months to heal, but the good news is you don't need the crutches." Happy day! More tears! No cancer, no MS, no hip replacement, no Guillain–Barré, no wheelchair, no crutches. Happy dance (ouch, my hip and back)!

In the meantime, those green drinks were working. I was starting to get more feeling back in my arms and legs! I also started getting curious about health. I was surprised at how quickly eating healthy was healing my body. The more I learned about health the more fascinated I was. I studied health for years and ended up writing a book about it called *101 Things I Wish I Knew Before*

I Fed My Children. I'm very grateful for all that I learned about health. I am now healthier than I've ever been inside and out and the weight issues I used to struggle with are gone! Hooray! My son asked me the other day if he could officially call me a health nut. I said, YES! I am now the healthiest eater I've ever met! My medical doctor says she wants to be like me when she grows up because she can't believe how good my blood test, BMI, etc. are. She also likes my healthy exercise habits, no caffeine, no alcohol etc.

As my hip got better, I was also seeing a lot of healers for my back pain. I was seeing kinesiologists, a body worker, chiropractors, acupuncturists, physical therapists, someone fix me up, please! The kinesiologist assigned walking. Ha! Not easy with a torn hip ligament. My goal was to walk out the back door of my house to my garden fence and back which was about 200 feet each way. This was amazingly hard to do, and so painful! Eventually, the hip did heal, and I got up to walking for about 40 minutes on the treadmill. Did I say I was walking 40 minutes on the treadmill each day? Actually, 40 minutes was my maximum time. Reporting that number is like when you are on a diet and you hit your goal weight and never see that number again. 40 minutes on the treadmill turned to 30 minutes, and then to 20, then to 10, and then to "My back hurts so badly. Why?"

By December 2014, 16 months after my accident, I was having more x-rays and thinking that I might have to have back surgery. All my holistic methods of healing were not giving me enough pain relief to live my life or even sit in a chair. In January 2015, I called to make an appointment with a surgeon; the first opening they had was April 22, 2015. I decided to wait, as I really wanted to see the *best* surgeon, not just any surgeon.

By the end of January, I was not sure I could survive until April, and I dug out all the old painkillers they had given me in the hospital when I first broke my back 17 months earlier. I'm not a big fan of medication, and I figured if I could deal with the pain without them I would, but I had reached the I-can't-deal-with-it spot. I'm very sensitive to medication and those pain killers put me to sleep. I actually slept for the entire month of February 2015. Luckily, my body got used to them, somehow, just in time for me to wake up for the crazy hot real estate market that started in March.

I actually paid people to drive me, laying on ice packs, to my real estate appointments. When my clients would ask me to sit down, I jokingly told them I don't like to sit. The truth was I could not sit because it hurt too bad, and I'd stand at the kitchen counter making my presentation and then get driven home crying because of the pain. Those were crazy days.

I called the surgeon's office, begging them to get me in sooner, and they snuck me in the back door by seeing the surgeon's PA. Of course, when I saw her, what did she want? New x-rays, new MRI, CAT scan, bone density test, blood tests, pain doctor for pain injections and more pain pills, etc. My husband, mom, and friends drove me to all these appointments as I lay in the back of the car on ice packs. It was really embarrassing speaking with all these doctors because in the past when I'd get frustrated, I'd cry; and boy, was I frustrated! I wanted to be out of pain and wanted my life back! Every doctor I saw got to see the sobbing, crazy lady act, which was embarrassing, but I could not hold it in. Unfortunately, the surgeon was concerned that my back pain was lower than the broken spot and was not sure that the surgery would help. He asked me to get other opinions. I saw two more surgeons and they said the same thing, but with a bit more confidence that surgery would help my pain.

In the meantime, I had about 10 escrows in process in my real estate business. It was a very busy spring home selling season. I decided to have surgery with the 3rd surgeon I saw. I needed to wait for some real estate work to finish, so I scheduled the surgery for May 18, 2015, the Monday after 8 of the 10 escrows had closed. I got my real estate partner to cover the remainder. Reading this now, I wonder why I was trying to work at all. One was to pay my bills, another was to service my clients. I was not taking a little time off. This was years of pain and working helped to take my mind off my sad state.

The surgery went well, minus a lung puncture that was not in the plan and added an extra hour to the surgery sewing my lung back up. The surgeon fused the L2-L3 vertebrae and replaced the disk in-between with a synthetic one. I was stitched up in 6 different places on my back and side 7 hours later. Recovery was pretty tough! I felt like I'd been hit by a train! I remember them saying that I had to sit up in the hospital the first day after surgery. Sitting sounded like an impossible task as my body felt so beat up and really unmovable. Before I knew it, I was sitting up, then walking with a walker and headed back home to recover.

Everyone back home and friends asked how I felt and if the surgery fixed my pain. It was really hard to tell at first because I had so much surgery pain. However, the day came that the surgery pain was low enough that I could feel for certain that my original pain was still there. That was a very sad day! I went back to all the things I was doing before to heal heal, only now, with post surgery pain. Pool exercising, physical therapy, healing lasers with chiropractors, acupuncture and massage. I knew I needed to try something different, but what? What would fix this burning back pain that didn't allow me to sit down or live my life?

I begged and pleaded with God to help me find the right person who could help me. After years of searching, I finally met him. A wonderful 87-year-old medical doctor turned kinesiologist. This would be the 3rd kinesiologist I had seen about my back and I was losing hope that this was the right modality for me. I was praying that this would be the person who could help me to relieve my suffering. I had doubt after so many failed attempts at pain relief. Some people recommended that I accept the fact that I'd always be in pain. I could not do that. I wanted to be pain free and was prepared to go to the ends of the earth until I found a cure for my pain.

I was referred to Dr. Warren Jacobs MD and Kinesiologist. He asked me why I was there, and I told him I wanted to sit in a chair, I wanted to get rid of the excruciating pain. I wanted to sit at church, exercise, go places with my family, have a social life, and get off prescription painkillers. The work began! Dr. Jacobs started testing my system via muscle testing, asking my subconscious mind what was causing the pain. Based on my systems response to his questions, he quickly showed me with a muscle test that all my pain was emotional not physical. Wait, what? How could that be?

I told him that I'm a pretty mellow person with a pretty good life, glossing over all the childhood and marriage issues. I didn't have any issues, well maybe a couple, but doesn't everyone have a few things? I don't see anyone but me standing in the back of rooms because they can't sit. This can't be emotional pain. I broke my back! It's structural pain I thought. Any movement aggravates my back, so how could the pain be emotional pain showing up as physical pain? That did not make sense to me. Dr. Jacobs informed me that a lot of things don't make sense, but that doesn't mean those things are not true. Look at nature. It's amazingly complex and just because we don't understand it does not mean it doesn't work. I told him I was desperate for relief and was willing to try his method, which was mostly talking about my buried emotions! Eek!

Dr. Jacobs asked me about my childhood which I said I don't really talk about. He asked me about my marriage which I told him I also don't really talk about. Why didn't I talk about these things? They were painful and I would cry a lot if I talked about them. Actually, I'd sob like a baby and would not even be able to speak! Instead I just repressed all these feelings and didn't think or talk about them. I'd turn my focus elsewhere and try not to remember the pain. 6 visits later, after telling him everything about my childhood and marriage and going through a case of his tissues while I sobbed, I was at home standing at my desk working (because it hurts to sit) and my back pain that felt like flames shut off. It just stopped! Like when you turn a light switch from on to off. I freaked out with excitement and yelled for Dusty and the kids and to tell them the thrilling news!

After that day, a slighter pain would come and go. It never returned with a vengeance like the original pain, but felt more like cramping and tight muscles. I worked to continue to learn how to shut that pain off. I learned the pain was being caused by me. I was feeling my emotional pain as physical pain. It was actually my thoughts, especially my subconscious thoughts, that were causing this tension in my body. As I learned this and started accepting and dealing with emotions instead of repressing them, I could keep that tension away. I started sitting, having a social life and even went back to yoga. What an enormous blessing and what an odd, shocking way to get it!

After becoming pain free, did you hear that? Yes, pain free. My next battle was getting off painkillers. I didn't realize I was addicted to the hydrocodone I'd been talking every 4 hours day and night for over a year. I thought I could just stop taking the pills once the pain was gone. Boy, was I wrong. I wanted those painkillers! I realized that I would probably lie, cheat or even steal to get them if I needed to. Wow, that was a scary feeling.

I asked Dr. Jacobs if he could help me get over this dependency. He recommended I take the painkillers every 4.5 hours instead of every 4 and then stretch it to 5 hours and so on. The problem was at about 4 hours and 1 minute I felt like I was about to have a panic attack and I'd run for the bottle of pills. The next time I saw Dr. Jacobs I told him my experience and we muscle tested to see what could help me. A muscles test is like a built-in lie detector test. When something is true to your system your muscles hold strong and when something is untrue, the electrical signal between the brain and muscles is disrupted and it's a lot harder for your muscles to stay strong. This is a method used by many chiropractors and kinesiologists to find answers from your own system (body, mind, spirit.)

Something truly does happen with your system when you lie. Dr. Jacobs asked my system why I kept taking the pills with a muscle test. My guess was that I was taking the pills because I had developed a dependency on them. The muscle test didn't hold on that statement meaning my system was saying that was not a true statement for me. My next guess was that I was taking the pills because I was afraid to be in pain if I didn't take them. The muscles test showed false. I guessed again that I was taking them because I was afraid of the withdrawals.

The muscle test didn't hold so that was not true either. I said I didn't know why I was taking them then. We asked my system by guessing. Is it a person? The muscle test showed yes. Which person? Dusty? The muscle test showed yes. Our bad relationship? The muscle test showed yes. If I stop taking these pills that numb me from life, I'd have to deal with our relationship? The muscle test showed yes. Oh my goodness! I sat there surprised and fascinated. I'm taking these pain pills to cover my marriage pain. Wow! I never took another pain pill from that moment forward. 10 days of panic attacks and throwing up withdrawals followed but I was ready to deal with my life.

Next, I noticed that my back pain would flair back up when I'd go to my desk to work on real estate. I knew that this pain I was feeling was actually my system trying to tell me something. That something was to stop doing things you don't like to do! If you no longer like real estate, do something you do like! I kept ignoring it until I could no longer go to my desk. My system would no longer allow me to ignore myself. What was I going to do if not real estate?

I did some muscle testing with Doctor Jacobs to figure out my new career. I thought it might have something to do with healthy eating as I had turned to plant-based eating, wrote a book about it, *101 Things I Wish I Knew Before I Fed My Children,* and loved sharing plant-based recipes and photos with friends and online. The muscles test showed that was not the right field for me. I was surprised. I guessed and guessed, but could not figure out what job I should do. Almost jokingly I said to Dr. Jacobs, I should do what you do. The muscle test held strong! Wait, what? I should become a kinesiologist?

I decided to take a course called Touch for Health which was the foundation of his work and then he created his own program that went with it. I took that foundation class which was very different from Dr. Jacobs work. I started practicing with friends and family and loved it. I still felt like something was missing however. My clients were feeling improvements, but I wanted something life changing like what I had experienced with Dr. Jacobs for my clients.

I kept looking for modalities that could stop the tug of war I felt going on inside me so often. I mostly felt mad, bad, in pain and sad my whole life, but put on a happy face and told everyone I was great. I wanted to fix how I felt on the inside and I wanted to fix my marriage!

Dr. Jacobs told me he heard about a process called PSYCH-K®. When he said PSYCH-K® I knew that was my word. I had a gut feeling about it. Dusty and I were really struggling, worse than ever before. I was tired of the struggle as it had been 20 years now. I decided I wanted to go stay in a hotel and make a plan, an escape plan from my marriage. This was the most brutal decision of my life. I believe in family. I wanted to make our marriage work. I had tried for 20 years! I had suffered for 20 years. Our oldest daughter was off on an 18-month church mission teaching people about God's love and how the family is central to God's plan of happiness. How would I tell my daughter what was going on back home? Could I not tell her and keep a secret as not to mess with the beautiful work she was doing? The only thing harder than staying in the marriage was ending it.

Thankfully, God helped me find a PSYCH-K® course that same week I was planning to leave my marriage. I was able to stay in a hotel to give myself some breathing room and thinking time to focus on the class and reprogram my limiting subconscious beliefs. I totally forgot to make my marriage escape plan because I was distracted by this subconscious change process I was learning. It was simple, powerful and effective. I decided this is what I wanted to do for my new career. I bought a domain name, BalancedYou. org and started making plans to change careers after the first day of class. I was so excited to have found my new passion!

When I got back home from the course, the most amazing thing happened. I looked at my husband and all I saw was love. I saw his goodness. I remembered the happy times. I was excited to see him. Three days earlier I was planning to leave him. How could everything be so different so quickly? He had not changed, I had. I was seeing him with a new perspective. I was seeing him through the lens of love, compassion, wholeness, oneness. He looked beautiful to me. I realized all this time, the issues were not with him, they were with me. I was broken, and this process made me whole again. I was reacting to him through my lens of a broken, hurting and wounded person full of limiting and negative programming. When we would interact, he was reacting to my reactions and then I was reacting to him. When I changed, he changed. Our marriage was healed in one weekend and I was the only participant in the change process. I was blown away!

I started to feel happy, joyful, calm, peaceful and wonderful all the time. If Dusty would forget to take out the trash I'd think, "hmm, he forgot to take out the trash, oh well." In the past, when he'd forget to take out the trash I'd think he didn't love me. He lied to me and said he would take out the trash just so I'd quit nagging him. He didn't really care about me or I must not be good enough to even remember to do a chore for, etc. I'd get mad and he'd get mad back and we'd go around and around. The cycle was now broken. Him forgetting to take out the trash had nothing to do with me! I was free!

I was so obsessed with this subconscious mind reprogramming process that as the real estate calls were coming in, I didn't want to take them. Even if someone wanted me to sell their million-dollar house, I was not interested. I told Dusty I wanted to stop selling real estate and open a business helping others reprogram their minds. This was very scary for my self-esteem as it meant giving up my large income, selling our big house, and moving into one of our rental properties so we could live on his income while I got my new business rolling. I had built my self-worth on my success and the stuff I could buy. If I changed careers and went from multiple six figures to zero, things were going to change drastically. Sweetly, he agreed and I put a for sale sign in my own front yard.

Within about 30 days, I took the first three PSYCH-K® courses. I started practicing with family, friends, and anyone who would let me help them reprogram their minds. Once I started feeling pretty comfortable with the subconscious change process, I slowly started charging for my services. I wrapped up the last few real estate deals I was going to handle, sold our house, and we moved into our rental property.

I stopped selling real estate on a Friday and was seeing clients for my new business, Balanced You, on Monday. It was weird at first. I felt like an actress in a movie doing a totally different job, but I loved it. I had to be careful when I answered my phone to say my new company name. I had been selling real estate for so long that it was hard to say "Balanced You" as my old subconscious program was to say, "RE/MAX" every time I picked up the phone!

I was so passionate about my new business and still am! I love watching people transform right in front of my very eyes. I watch clients overcoming chronic physical and emotional pain, depression, anxiety, allergies, and dis-ease. I see them healing relationships and finding relationships they were longing for. I see them overcoming trauma and drama, fears, phobias, and stress. I see their businesses and job positions improving dramatically and quickly. I see them healing their self-esteem, finding their personal power and realizing their divinity. I see them double their sales and create more money, more time, more freedom and residual incomes. They have the same transformative results I had.

They think I am a miracle worker, but they are the miracle workers. The power of the subconscious mind is fascinating and when you put that power to work for you, you can change anything you want in your life. You can even rewrite your genes! What a thrill and a joy to support people as they become the best version of themselves by shedding their subconscious limiting beliefs, realizing who they really are and following their passions in life. I could not be more blessed to know what I know and be able to share it with others.

Subconscious change has helped me to reprogram my mind, to get rid of all my physical and emotional pain, get off pain killers, save my marriage, rebuild my self-esteem and brought joy, peace and happiness back into my life. We had new family photos taken recently by the amazing Marcy Browe and it's wonderful and sad to think that if I had not found this process, those family photos would have never happened. The interesting thing was our photographer kept commenting on what a lovely and happy family we were. She said in an email to me later, "I told you this in person, but I think you have one of the most wonderful families I have ever encountered. You must be bursting with pride."

It's true. I did, and I do, but my limiting beliefs kept me from seeing that. I was so wrapped up in my own emotional pain and that was all I could see. I thank God for this process. I can't even begin to explain how good my life is now. I literally pinched myself the other day when I was driving just to make sure this was real life because it feels like a dream. I never knew life could feel so good. What a blessing to tap into the power of the subconscious mind and literally change my world.

CHAPTER 3

MY TRIP TO THE BIRD HOUSE

Scan the QR code or follow this link to watch the video for this chapter. https://youtu.be/Li-24o-2-H8

They say desperate times call for desperate measures. Before I found pain relief through mind reprogramming, I was getting desperate for pain relief. Chronic pain is depressing, debilitating, frustrating, maddening and painful! My physical pain had increased so much that I was having trouble just being alive. There was no break from my pain. It was all day and all night, 24/7. I could not enjoy anything as I was in so much pain all the time. Some things would make it worse, but nothing seemed to make it any better. Unfortunately, the surgery didn't help my pain, nor did the chiropractic, acupuncture, kinesiology, physical therapy, massages, water exercises, meditation, creams, rubs, pain patches, pain injections or pain pills. What was left to try to help my pain? The doctors kept prescribing more and more pain pills. These pills were intense. I remember one time asking my husband if he was floating too, or if it was just me and I was not exaggerating! These pills made me sleepy, crazy, forgetful, and unable to function. Then someone asked me if I had tried CBD. I didn't know what that was and later found out it was the non-psychogenic portion of the marijuana plant and was supposed to help with pain relief and have no negative side effects. I was having lots of side effects from my pain pills, but I was a bit uncomfortable with the CBD option.

I was not sure I was willing to try CBD as I lived by a strict health code due to our religion. I have never even tasted coffee, let alone alcohol or drugs. I didn't believe in illegal drugs and didn't want to put a drug into my body. Then I was thinking this was now legal and it was the non-psychogenic part of a plant. Really it was not worse, maybe better than the legal drugs I was taking. I decided to give it a try.

I looked online and found a company that offered CBD. Dusty drove me there to pick some up, as driving was excruciatingly painful. When we got there, it was a liquor store, to which neither of us had ever entered being members of the Church of Jesus Christ of Latter-Day Saints. I walked inside and asked for "The Bird House" as I'd been instructed to do over the phone. The man in the liquor store told me it was outside the door to the right. I started walking around the building in the dark thinking this is supposed to be legal, but it sure does not feel legal. I arrive at "The Bird House" door and went inside. My heart was pounding. Inside was a person behind bullet proof glass. I say, "I'm here to get some CBD." He replies, "please show me your prescription." I say, "what prescription? I do not have a prescription." He hands me a list of doctors who will give me a prescription and asks me to go to one of them and come back tomorrow.

The next day I head to the "doctor." A middle eastern woman in an office building ½ a mile from my real estate office, who greets me. I'm starting to think I should be doing these things in an unmarked vehicle instead of in my car with my advertisements on the side. I had just been in a real estate meeting earlier that week, standing in the back because I could not sit due to my pain. They were discussing trying to get rid of "dispensaries" that were popping up around the city bringing in riff-raff. I tried not to look guilty. I surely was not riff-raff. I was in pain, desperate and probably the type of person they legalized this stuff for in the first place.

I filled out a medical questionnaire after passing hallways of what appeared to be riff raff. I tell the "doctor" that I have severe pain and I want to try some CBD to see if it helps. She offers me a prescription for 1-3 years based on how much money I want to give her. I told her I'd just like to try it once, but she said a year is the shortest time I could purchase, so I did. She tried to sell me the three year prescription, but I didn't want it, nor could I bear the thought of being in pain for three more years.

Later that night, my husband and I headed back to "The Bird House." This time I got in with my prescription and entered this hazy neon green lit room with a display counter of all the products I could choose from. No one else in "The Bird House," from what I could tell, seemed to be in chronic pain looking for pain relief. They seemed to be the same people I saw at the "doctor's" office; young adults wanting to get high.

I asked the young girl at the counter, thinking about how grateful I was that my teenage daughters didn't work there, what CBD products they had. She gave me a liquid dropper vial of CBD oil and tried to throw in some "free additional products", like THC brownies. No thank you! I paid and quickly got out of there.

When we got home, I opened the CBD oil and smelled it. Wow, that is one strong smell. I didn't think I would be able to swallow something that smelled that gross! The next day I went to the health food store and got some empty capsules and put some CBD oil in one before bed and swallowed my first CBD pill. Besides burping nasty CBD oil all night, I felt quite relaxed and slept pretty well. I was pleasantly surprised.

I looked online again to see if I could find the powdered CBD capsules to avoid the oil capsules I was making. I found a company and arranged a meet up point in a parking lot by a local Chinese restaurant. This all felt so foreign coming from my strict background of morals and values, but I was desperate.

I arrived in the parking lot and waited in my car. A stranger gets in my car and hands me a small envelope with a vile of CBD pills in it. I handed him cash and he gets out of my car. This is crazy! If this is legal, why does this feel so illegal?

That night I took one of the pills and had the same experience. I felt extra relaxed and slept well that night. The next morning, I decided to take another instead of my normal pain pills. Being awake, I realized that I was not feeling totally normal, not normal at all, actually, and I was feeling dizzy and floaty which was the feeling I was trying to avoid with my pain pills. It's much easier to get CBD now and it's better regulated, so you know what you are getting. I know many people who have good results with it, but for me, I decided to go back to my pain pills. I hid the CBD pills in the back of my home office desk and never touched them again.

I'm so thankful that I have now found out what was really causing my pain and that I no longer needed a pill of any sort to cover my pain because my pain is gone. I wish this blessing on you too. I believe that with the power of the mind, you can overcome anything, even chronic pain. My oldest daughter is always asking me, mom what about this, can reprogramming the mind help this? What about this? What about that? I always give her the same answer.

Our subconscious mind controls every part of us. It controls our lives, health, happiness, relationships, success, spirituality, grief, loss, self-esteem, and personal power. The list goes on and on. I have never found anything that the subconscious mind change process can't help EXCEPT for someone who does not want to change. Some people are completely wrapped up in their problems. Their problems become their identity. They may say they don't like their problems and they want out of them, but if I offer to help, they will probably give me some excuse of why they can't see me or one of my facilitators at Balanced You. Most of the time the notion of holding onto their problems is completely subconscious.

Most people consciously want a better life. But if they have subconscious beliefs that they are to remain unhappy, unhealthy and poor in any definition of the word, they sometimes won't let go of those limiting beliefs to move into a new life and a new reality. I hope more people will learn about the power of the mind and make changes before their pain gets too bad to bear.

If you only knew how much better your life could be with the power of your subconscious mind working for you instead of against you, you'd schedule your mind reprogramming today. Just like your computer and cell phone need updates, so does your mind. You are walking around with lenses, filters, and beliefs that were put there as a child. It's time to see the world the way you want it to appear. If you want to change your view, you've got to change your lens.

So, what do you want different in your life? If I had a magic wand and you got three wishes, what would they be? What do you want? What do you want your life to look like, sound like, feel like? We send out an energetic signal of what we want and then we attract that to ourselves. The subconscious does not understand negative, so if you are wishing for what you don't want or continuously thinking about what you don't want, your subconscious is actually creating that reality for you. What you focus on appears. If you think about what you do want, you are creating that reality. If you program what you do want into your subconscious mind, it becomes your new reality.

Have you ever heard of the book or movie *The Secret? The Secret,* https://en.wikipedia.org/wiki/The_Secret_(book), is that you create what you think about and you create how you are feeling. *The Secret* teaches that if you want something, you have to ask for it. Ask God, or the Universe, or the highest power you believe in for what you want. Then believe that you will get it. You have to believe like you've never believed before and feel as if you have that thing you want already in your life. Before you even receive it, you have to be grateful for it because you know it's on it's way into your life and you are so excited and thankful. This is a very powerful process and I believe in it! The hard part for most, is keeping up the faith until what you want shows up. When you start to doubt, you push that thing back instead of pulling it in. Lucky for us, the subconscious mind is the shortcut to this process.

The subconscious is one million times more powerful than the conscious mind and controls us 95-99% of the day. If you put that much power into what you want, it's going to happen for you much quicker and with a lot less effort on your part! I believe in shortcuts! If we can help you improve your life in an easier way, let's do it!

How about you? Are you ready for a shortcut to happiness and success in your life? I know, this may sound too good to be true. My own friends tell me that if they didn't watch me transform in front of their own eyes, they would not even believe my story. When I help clients transform, they ask if I've called their spouse, children, boss and friends and told everyone to act differently around them and to treat them exactly as they wish to be treated. NO! I don't do that. That would be way too much work and you know someone would mess it up. Reprogramming the mind changes the print out of your life. It's that powerful!

CHAPTER 4

WHERE DOES PAIN COME FROM?

Scan the QR code or follow this link to watch the video
for this chapter. https://youtu.be/WCB8Xi0rSUU

I spent many of my elementary school days in the nurse's office. My tummy was always hurting. I didn't know why my tummy hurt. I thought something was wrong with my tummy. My nose was always bleeding. I thought something was wrong with my nose. When I hit puberty, I had horrible cramps. I thought something was wrong with my female organs. My mom took me to the doctor to "talk" about my female pain. A pair of rubber gloves later and my look of death towards my mother, the doctor said nothing seemed wrong with my female parts and prescribed pain pills.

I had issues with weight gain. I thought something was wrong with my metabolism. I suffered with back pain. I thought something was wrong with my back. I suffered with headaches. I thought something was wrong with my head. I suffered with endometriosis. I thought something was wrong with my uterus. I suffered with a racing heart. I thought something was wrong with my heart. I suffered with yeast infections, bladder infections and bacterial infections. I thought my body could not fight off germs. I suffered with ulcers in my bladder and stomach. I thought something was wrong with my bladder and stomach.

Then they told me I had interstitial cystitis. I knew something else was wrong with my bladder. I suffered with allergies. I thought something was wrong with my digestive tract. I suffered with liver failure. I knew something was wrong with my liver. Then I broke my back. I knew something was wrong with my back. Then doctors found a black spot in my left hip bone. I thought something was wrong with my bone. Then they told me I had osteopenia. I thought something was wrong with my bone density. I was always sick with colds and flus. I thought something was wrong with my immune system. I spent so much money trying to solve all these medical conditions and fix myself. As soon as I'd take care of one health issue another would appear.

I had zero idea that there was any connection between my emotions and my physical body. I did not understand the mind/ body connection. I hid my emotions pretty well, even from myself. I knew I felt mad, bad, sad, sick, in pain and frustrated most of my life, but that was the extent of my understanding. I'd put on a happy face and tell everyone I was GREAT! Back then I thought that's what positive affirmations were. I didn't realize I was just lying to myself and everyone else.

After I had healed myself from all my physical symptoms with subconscious change, I found Louise Hay. I especially love her little pocket guide to all that ails you called *Heal Your Body*. I looked up my previous symptoms in her condition lists and this is what she says is the emotional cause of my ailments. http://alchemyofhealing. com/causes-of-symptoms-according-to-louise-hay/.

Stomach: Holds nourishment. Digests ideas. Dread. Fear of the new. Inability to assimilate the new.

Bleeding: Joy running out. Anger.

Cramps: Tension. Fear. Gripping, holding on.

Fat or Weight issues: Oversensitivity. Often represents fear and shows a need for protection. Fear may be a cover for hidden anger and a resistance to forgive. Running away from feelings. Insecurity, self-rejection and seeking fulfillment. – Hips: Lumps of stubborn anger at the parents. – Thighs: Packed childhood anger. Often rage at the father.

Mid-Back Pain: Guilt. Stuck in all that stuff back there. "Get off my back!"

Headaches: Invalidating the self. Self-criticism. Fear.

Heart: Represents the center of love and security.

Bladder Problems: Anxiety. Holding on to old ideas. Fear of letting go. Being "pissed off".

Urinary infections: Pissed off, usually at the opposite sex or a lover. Blaming others.

Uterus: Represents the home of creativity.

Vaginitis: Anger at a mate. Sexual guilt. Punishing the self.

Infection: Irritation, anger, annoyance.

Constipation: Incomplete releasing. Holding on to garbage of the past. Guilt over the past. Sometimes stinginess.

Gas: Gripping. Fear. Undigested ideas.

Liver: Seat of anger and primitive emotions. Chronic complaining. Justifying fault-finding to deceive yourself. Feeling bad.

Bones: Represent the structure of the universe.

Bone marrow: Represents deepest beliefs about the self. How you support and care for yourself.

Bone Breaks: Rebelling against authority.

Colds: Too much going on at once. Mental confusion, disorder. Small hurts.

Wow! I was blown away! I had no idea that all my years of emotional suffering were causing my physical suffering. I thought I was just the unluckiest person and had to endure both physical and emotional pain. When I got rid of the emotional pain, the physical pain went away, too. Why didn't a doctor ever tell me about this? I guess it's not the western medical model. Allopathic medicine looks to treat or suppress symptoms with pharmacology. https://en.wikipedia.org/wiki/Allopathic_medicine.

I'm guessing, self-healing by looking at your life, and changing your mind and thought patterns, as well as your food, the fuel you put into your amazing system to keep it running property, is not a profitable offering in Western medicine so they don't learn it or mention it. What a shame. I'm not saying doctors and medicine are not important, I am grateful for all the times they've helped me. I just wish during all my years of pain, one of them would have mentioned the ideas I'm sharing with you.

According to Dr. Michael Greger, in his "Uprooting the Leading Causes of Death" presentation, I noted that the side effects from prescription drugs kill an estimated 100,000 Americans every year, making medical care the sixth leading cause of death in the United States. There are another 7,000 deaths from getting the wrong medicine by mistake and 20,000 deaths from other errors in hospitals. Hospitals are dangerous places. An additional 99,000 of us die yearly from hospital-acquired infections. http://bit.ly/3rdCauseOfDeath

There is also an opioid epidemic going on. People are hurting and doctors are prescribing pain pills. Why are they hurting? Their pain, like mine, may be emotional pain showing up physically. Opioids cover emotional pain too. They numb you so you feel better physically and emotionally. I believe that is why so many people get addicted. It stops the emotional pain. Sadly, death by opioid overdose is now the number one killer of US citizens under 50 years old with over 65,000 deaths per year. http://bit.ly/Oepidemic.

For our own health and safety, we need to take healing back into our own hands. We have the power to change. Our genes do not completely define us. We can control our genes and gene expression and gene rewriting with the power of the subconscious mind. We don't need someone else to fix us, (unless we need critical medical care like stitches.) We have the power to change our lives and our health.

Are you ready to start your journey to great health and wellbeing? You can get my no-cost pain workbook here as well as a 30-minute complimentary Balanced You intro call, https://transformmypain.com/.

I was fascinated when I heard the story of Dr. Joe Dispenza. He was a young chiropractor who had a terrible biking accident during a triathlon. Four different doctors told him he needed immediate surgery to prevent paralysis due to his many broken vertebrae and the chance of the bone shards pressing into his spinal cord and paralyzing him permanently. Dr. Dispenza had learned through chiropractic about the body's amazing ability to heal itself. Dr. Dispenza did not listen to the surgeons, but instead decided to lay face down and visualize himself healing for as long as it took. As he describes in his book *You Are the Placebo*, only 9 weeks later, he was back to work. He healed himself with his mind, belief and gratitude. What an amazing example of the power of the mind to heal our bodies.

I also love the work of Dr. John Sarno who saw 10,000 chronic pain patients over 25 years and documented with follow up calls that 90% of them overcame their pain and remained pain free. Dr. Sarno describes that their physical pain was their subconscious mind trying to block emotions by sending physical pain to the body with a process of ischemia. This is a process the system uses in an attempt to distract the person from their subconscious emotions coming to surface. There was actually nothing physically wrong with his patients, even if the medical doctor found an abnormality in their imaging. That abnormality was not causing the pain. Maybe in the beginning there was something physically wrong with them. Maybe they did have an injury, but our bodies heal.

Sometimes we think they don't heal because we still feel pain, but Dr. Sarno explains that it's typical that we are feeling pain for another reason, an emotional reason. Our very smart system tends to send the pain to the injury spot keeping us believing there is something wrong with that place on our bodies. Many of us have physical abnormalities in our bodies that we do not even know about. Most abnormalities do not cause pain or issues. Our bodies are meant to heal when they are injured, and they do. Only 5% of people are born with disease. So why are there so many people sick and suffering and why do almost all of us die of disease? It's due to our subconscious blocking emotions. Interestingly, it could be positive or negative emotions. Both can be overwhelming. So how do we take our health back into our own hands?

Chronic pain is not a physical issue according to Dr. Sarno. If you are still not sure about this theory, I highly recommend his book, *Healing Back Pain* which covers not only back pain, but all types of pain. His book, *The Mind Body Prescription,* is great too! The main point of the book is to understand and believe how our subconscious mind, or unconscious mind he calls it, uses physical pain to block emotion. Dr. Sarno shared that 20% of his pain patients were able to overcome their pain with a deep understanding of this process. The other 80% need a process like ours at *Balanced You,* to reprogram the mind and overcome the pain at a subconscious level.

My system would send emotional pain to my back after I broke it. So I assumed something was still wrong with my back. Even after major surgery and years of healing I thought the doctors must have been missing something. I guess they were missing something! They were missing that my physical pain was being caused by my emotional pain.

Dr. Sarno shares that it is not enough to deal with your emotions, you also have to realize that the pain is coming from repressed emotions, especially anger and rage. If you are willing to look into what you might be suppressing and believe that this suppression is the cause of your pain, that is the start of pain relief.

The beautiful part is that you don't have to relive your pain to deal with it emotionally, you just have to transform your perception of it. How would you prefer to feel about that person, situation or event that is causing some dis-ease in your system? Wouldn't you rather feel loving, accepting, forgiving, understanding, or peaceful?

Let us help you program that into your subconscious and don't be surprised if that frees you from your pain.

My oldest daughter believed she had severe allergies to eggs, nuts, gluten and dairy. The more stress she had in her life the worse the "allergies" got. Her body was playing a trick on her. Her system figured out that if it reacted after she ate, she'd blame her stomach aches, headaches, and rashes on food. It was the perfect trick! Once we figured out the trick her body was playing on her, I helped her reprogram her subconscious issues. Her "allergies" were gone! She can now eat the foods she once had to avoid, reaction free. Fascinating!

The same thing happened with me. I thought I was allergic to gluten for 10 years and avoided it due to severe digestive issues. After I learned this mind reprogramming process, I quickly and easily got rid of my gluten intolerance. I found my gluten issues were tied to a thought I had before my 4th pregnancy. Once I changed my perception of that thought, I could eat all the gluten I wanted. I could not eat bell peppers before learning how to reprogram the mind. I'd burp for days. Now I enjoy bell peppers reaction free.

I was working with a client recently on relationships and finding the relationship she wanted to attract into her life. As we worked, she said, "I know this seems weird, but I got a really sharp pain in my back when we were speaking about letting go. Isn't that weird?" I replied, "No, that is not weird at all! I've learned that our system reacts with pain when it's trying to distract us from feeling strong emotions." I asked her if there was something having to do with a relationship that she needed to let go of, and she told me she could think of one thing. Without getting into any details we did some mind reprogramming on that one issue and immediately the pain in her back was gone.

I see over and over with our clients that their emotional pain turns to physical pain. I also see that their pain goes to their physical injury locations. Take whiplash, for example. The neck should not hurt for 10 years after a car accident, but the trauma does last because the subconscious is timeless. This emotional pain likes to hang out in the old injury spots. We can help you to reprogram your mind to change your perception of the accident or injury and transform the trauma that is still causing negative reactions in the subconscious mind and pain in the physical body. I had a sweet older gentleman who used a cane in my office recently. After our session, he walked out holding the cane above his head. He no longer needed it for support, or balance after helping him reprogram some emotional pain. Fascinating!

I feel blessed that people now hire the facilitators at *Balanced You,* who help them reprogram their minds to overcome their emotional and physical pain, and to create the life and success of their dreams. What a blessing to share this with others.

I have discovered that my purpose is to help others live their purpose. People who are suffering physically and emotionally typically don't live their purpose as their pain throws them off course. I feel blessed that my team and I can help reprogram their subconscious minds and get back to living their purpose.

At *Balanced You* we also love helping those that are pain free but feel like their life is lacking in some fashion. Maybe they need help with relationships, finances, spirituality, happiness, peace, forgiveness, or business success. You name it, we can help you reprogram your subconscious mind to accomplish all your goals.

CHAPTER 5

UNLEASHING THE POWER OF THE SUBCONSCIOUS MIND

Scan the QR code or follow this link to watch the video for this chapter. https://youtu.be/cQOoQQD4egA

I used to love watching the Oprah Winfrey Show back in the day when it was on weekday afternoons. That show was something I really looked forward to after a long day with my young kids. I remember how long those days were as I'd already be checking the clock by 7am, trying to figure out how many more hours I had till Dusty got home after work. I was terrible at entertaining myself and not much better at entertaining my kids. Luckily, I was blessed with creative kids, so they entertained me! I enjoyed watching Oprah because it got my mind thinking beyond ABC's and 123's. I must admit I use to be a bit saddened when she would have a show about a topic like the power of the mind. I'd usually skip watching those days because I really was not ready for all that information. I didn't believe it because I thought it was other people that were making me unhappy. I'd been saying positive affirmations for years with no results, so I didn't think I had the power to change my feelings and thoughts.

As I was searching the web the other day I found a video clip from 1993 with Oprah and Deepak Chopra, http://bit.ly/OprahAndDeepak. Deepak was showing Oprah how a pendulum works. With the power of your mind you can control how it swings. You are not consciously moving the dangling object, you are thinking about moving it and with the power of your mind, the subconscious goes to work to make the micro muscles in your fingers move ever so slightly to accomplish the goal. Oprah was blown away as she imagined the pendulum to swing one way and it did. Then she imagined it to swing the opposite way and it did. Then it moved in circles when she imagined it moving in circles and then the circles went the opposite way when she reversed her imagination. Oprah was fascinated and so was I, while watching this clip in 2018, but in 1993 I was not ready for this stuff!

The point of the pendulum demo is to show you the power of your subconscious mind. You give your mind an assignment and it performs. You really do control your reality. I loved the video so much I made one of my own, http://bit.ly/JennyPendulum.

This demo also shows you that you need to focus your mind to create results. As soon as you stop concentrating on the task at hand, the subconscious stops performing the operation. That is why what we do at *Balanced You* is so powerful. We help you reprogram your subconscious mind so it keeps its focus on accomplishing your goal even when your conscious mind moves on to something else. That way, 95-99% of the day and night your subconscious is pushing you to your goal.

Things don't happen to you, you create them from the inside out based on your subconscious programming. What about my car accident, my broken leg, or my bankruptcy? I could not and would not have created that we think! Sorry to break it to you, but actually, you did! Now, probably not consciously, but subconsciously. Your subconscious processes 40 million bits of information per second.

Psychology Today reports that 70%, http://bit.ly/NegativeMentalChatter, of those 40 million bits of mind processing are limiting beliefs. Imagine how much self-sabotage is going on! The pendulum worked in the demo when Oprah was focused on it. When she no longer focused on it, nothing happened. The same applies to our lives. We can keep things going well when we focus on them, but when we lose our focus because we are focused on other things, we are then subject to our programming. You can change your programming and change the printout of your life. YOU have the power! Isn't that the best news ever? Except for rare instances, it doesn't even matter what is in our genes. We can change it all!

Bruce Lipton, PhD cellular biologist says our subconscious runs the show 95-99% of the time and we are only consciously in charge 1-4% of the time. The power of the subconscious is helpful in so many ways because we can do so much without thought. We can walk, talk, drive, with zero conscious effort once we learn how to do it. The typing of this book right now is a perfect example of subconscious program. I'm not thinking about what buttons I need to press. Typing became a subconscious program for me. During high school, I checked out a typing book from the library and sat at my parent's typewriter each day practicing until I had it down. Yes, I'm that old! Now you can do it online with free typing programs! So easy.

Anther muscle memory I have is flute playing and reading sheet music. I played flute so much when I was young that now I can play once a year, and I never forget how to do it or how to read the music. You know the saying, it's like riding a bike. Once your subconscious gets it down, you can run that program automatically. Remember how much focus and effort and concentration it took when you learned to drive? Especially if you drove a stick shift! But once you have it down, you can talk on the phone, sing to the radio, or mentally plan out your next business meeting all while driving because the subconscious is doing the driving. It's that powerful.

Can you see how these "auto-pilot" programs in the subconscious could be detrimental as well as helpful? What if your automatic subconscious program is stress, fear, worry, anxiety, sickness, doubt, depression, unhappiness, loneliness, offensiveness, anger, judgement, untruth, abandonment, rage, addiction, failure, grief? How do you think you will automatically feel with those programs?

How do you know what your programs are? It's pretty easy, you look at yourself and your life. If you don't feel the way you want to feel, and if your life does not look like you want it to look, it's because you do not have a subconscious program to support these scenarios you want. If you believe something, and your subconscious is working 95-99% of the day to make that a reality, it's 95-99% chance that that is your reality. If you want something and are "trying" to get it during the 1-4% of the time that you are in conscious control of your life, you will most likely be wondering why you can't seem to accomplish that goal. You might feel like you are always getting in your own way. That is because you are. Not purposely of course, but subconsciously.

Where did you get all this programming anyway? You got this programming when you were in utero to around 7 years old. Your brain was in a theta state, which is like a hypnotic state. You were a sponge soaking up EVERYTHING. You didn't judge good or bad, you just absorbed the sights, sounds, feeling, experiences and you even were programmed by your mother's feeling while you were in utero.

Growing up, did you ever dislike something your parents did to you like spit on a napkin and wipe your face? You swore to yourself you'd never do that to your future children. But one day, you are walking into church with your kids and notice the dirt on your son's face. Guess who starts spitting on a tissue to wipe his face. You! You are doing the exact same things to your kid that you swore you would never do! We might do this in little ways like how we wipe our kids face, but we do it in larger ways, too. We follow the programming of what was modeled to us growing up automatically, unless we make a huge conscious effort to break the mold. We do this with our money, relationships, spirituality, health and the list goes on and on.

The fastest way to change your life is to change your subconscious programming. The subconscious can literally turn the bread you eat into bone. It's one powerful system! What else can it do? The subconscious is habitual. The subconscious monitors the operations of the body like heart rate, breathing, digestion, etc. The subconscious sees the world through the 5 senses (seeing, feeling, hearing, smelling and tasting.) The subconscious holds your long term memory and stores past experiences, beliefs, attitudes and values, but functions in the now. The subconscious is timeless. Past traumas are still current in the subconscious mind and typically have physical effects, especially health issues.

The subconscious is focused on the present only, but uses past learning to perform current functions like driving, talking, and walking. The subconscious processes 40 million bits of information per second and completes thousands of tasks at a time. The subconscious is programmable, but only with certain methods. Conscious thoughts or affirmations don't typically reprogram the subconscious mind.

The most exciting news I ever heard was that I could simply, powerfully and effectively change my programming. Even more exciting than that was that the process I found worked better than I could have ever imagined. It was pretty much as good as a magic wand. I had no idea how powerful my subconscious was until I programmed it to do what I wanted, and guess what? It worked! Fascinating! If you knew you could reprogram your subconscious mind and easily change anything in your life, how long would you wait to try out the process? I hope it's not long! You can change your health, wellness, finances, relationships, transform traumas and dramas, connect with your spirituality, easily build rapport, improve your communication, transform reactions, phobias, and create ultimate success with more money, more time and more freedom.

Even better, you don't have to go back and relive the past, you can change your programming to align with your conscious goals.

So why doesn't everyone just reprogram their subconscious mind? They say when the student is ready, the teacher will appear. The clients who have the hugest miracles with us are the ones who are ready to change. It took me a very long time to be ready for change. I didn't even want to hear about it. I even skipped my favorite show, the Oprah show, on the days she had the "Law of Attraction" type guests. I was not ready to look at myself in the mirror and make the changes I needed to make to change my life. I was too caught up in my own pain and the blame game. It was twenty plus years after that show on the power of the mind that I was ready to make my current life, the life of my dreams, and took the power that I had all along and put it to work for me.

I was at a business conference and there was a lady with a lot of foot pain from a recent surgery and said she needed to leave the conference we were at due to the pain she was feeling. I asked if I could help her possibly experience some pain relief and she excitedly agreed. We spent about 10 minutes reprogramming her mind and she said the pain disappeared and she was able to easily stay at the conference all day. She even stuck around for the night cap which went late! The power of the mind will knock your socks off! Most of my clients tell me that they wish they would have done it sooner!

I quickly learned that all subconscious change processes are not created equal and while they were all beneficial, I wanted something earth shattering. You know what they say, be careful what you wish for because you just might get it! And boy did I get it!

When you understand the power of the subconscious and find out that you can put that power house to work for you, watch out world! Now, the subconscious isn't really working against you, it just runs whatever programs it has until you replace these programs with something new, an upgrade if you will. A new program that would serve you better. The subconscious is your super-computer. It's extremely important to keep your supercomputer in line with your goals for maximum happiness and success.

What type of programming in your subconscious mind

could hurt you? How about some of these limiting beliefs: No matter what I do or how hard I try, it's never good enough. The decisions I make usually turn out wrong. If people knew the real me they wouldn't like me. I blame others (boss, spouse, parents, children etc.) for my problems. I shouldn't try anything new or risky because I'll probably screw it up. It's not safe to ask others to help me because I can't trust them to do the job right. My opinion doesn't really matter. What I do isn't really important. I'm not good enough. I'll never make enough money. I suffer from x,y,z, which runs in my family. I don't think my soulmate exists. I never feel happy. I can never catch a break. I never have enough time or money. Why are my relationships so hard? Everyone else always seems to get ahead. I'm not worth it. And the list goes on and on.

If you are having thoughts like these or outcomes like these, it may be time to update your programming. When you reprogram your subconscious mind, you can get out of your own way. The subconscious creates what it believes. What you are creating, is what you are believing. If you don't like your creation, change your belief system with the power of your mind.

I'm not talking about positive thoughts or affirmations to change your programming, I'm talking about rewriting the neural pathways in your brain. Sound scary? Not to worry, it's not! The first step in reprogramming your mind is to find out what you want. Most of us know what we don't like and don't want, but what DO we want? Decide what you want and write your goals out in a statement. Make your statements short, present tense, positively stated, and emotionally meaningful.

Some examples could be: I lovingly appreciate and accept myself. I love myself honestly and unconditionally. I am confident and self-assured. My sense of safety and security in the world comes from within. I am worthy of a passionate relationship. I am willing to risk loving and accept love. I enjoy having more money than I need. I see the good in myself and everyone around me. I am happy to be me. I am compassionate in my relationships. I am always healthy and full of energy. I love to eat healthy food and exercise. I lovingly let go of the past. I am calm and confident in business. I sleep easily and peacefully. I am confident and I excel at all I do. I easily make $x per month. I found my soulmate quickly and easily and we are enjoying a wonderful life together. I have so much free time now that I have a huge residual income. I am pain free.

While these may sound like positive affirmations, they are actually statements you can program into your subconscious. The best way to change your subconscious beliefs is to reprogram the subconscious mind. But how can you change the subconscious mind? You can learn the science behind the process in Bruce Lipton's fascinating book, *The Biology of Belief.*

Our subconscious is a huge benefit to us in so many ways. Our subconscious makes life more automated and much easier than if we had to focus intensely on every task every time we did it. Imagine if we had to concentrate to walk like we did when we first learned how. It would take all of our concentration to stay upright. All of our brain power would go to that task instead of a multitude of other things we can do as we walk freely without much thought. Thanks to our subconscious, we can go on auto pilot because of our subconscious programming.

Scientists have discovered that we function out of our subconscious mind 95-99% of our day. Truly we are acting, thinking, feeling, responding and being not based on what we want, but based on the programs in our mind. Imagine the adult who tries so hard to be successful, but for some reason they just seem to never get it right. Something seems to always block their success. This might be the same adult who as a child heard things like, "you'll never amount to anything" or "why do you always mess everything up?" or "you don't deserve that." This adult is trying with their conscious mind, (which runs 1-5% of the day,) to overpower the program that got recorded in the subconscious from their childhood.

If our subconscious programs and our conscious goals don't align, we are battling our own programming 95-99% of the time. Can you see why we struggle? Can you see why we get so frustrated with ourselves? Why we say things like, "starting Monday"...and "this time, I'm really going to stick with it." Don't get down on yourself, just change your programming.

How about the child who is programed with, "she's a sickly child," or "you're so hard to get along with, you'll probably always be alone." How do we get these thoughts out of our subconscious programming? How do we keep these subconscious programs from running our lives in a direction we don't want to take? One solution is to be more mindful. Think about where you are and what you are doing and be present. Function from your conscious mind, not your subconscious. Easier said than done, right?

In this busy, high tech, fast track time we live in, it's hard to be present! We fret over the past and worry about the future. Our minds are like spaghetti keeping track of our to-do lists. When you are sitting at a traffic light, what are you thinking about? Catch yourself next time and be more present.

After you work on being present, what more can you do? Ask yourself what you want to be different in your life. What's working, what's not working, and what you want to be working differently? Where are you now, where would you rather be? Consider these questions and ponder the answers. We'd love to discuss these questions with you in a 30 minute complimentary call. Schedule anytime at https://balancedyou.org/.

Do I believe in affirmations? For 20 years I said, "I am happy, I am healthy, I am terrific." I did not notice a change. I did notice I was lying to myself. I was not happy, healthy or terrific. I needed a process to change my program that was causing me to feel the opposite of my goal. An affirmation is repeating a conscious goal without reprogramming the subconscious. Ever try yelling at your computer because you don't like the program it's running? Did your computer change its programming when you yelled at it? NO! The same goes for your mind. You must upload a new program. Reprogramming the subconscious mind is the most simple, powerful and effective change process to rewrite old programs that are not serving you.

Take the time to reprogram your subconscious mind and be more mindful of how you speak, think, feel and act around others.

Be especially mindful around children. Not only are they watching you, but they are recording you and repeating the programs you teach them for the rest of their lives. Their minds are audio and video recorders. That's why 3 year old's can easily learn 3 languages and whichever language you speak to them, is what they speak. What money language are you teaching them? What self-esteem language are you teaching them? What relationship language are you teaching them? What a great responsibility we have to lift those around us, especially our children.

Be the person to give the children around you uplifting subconscious programs that will help them succeed in life, be the best they can be, and do what they were meant to do. Smile and let your eyes light up when you see them. Tell them you are so glad to know them. Stop what you are doing and listen when they speak to you. Be open and curious to their ideas and questions. Be patient and loving. How do you change the world? You positively program a child.

For good or bad, our influence reverberates endlessly throughout humanity. What mark do you want to leave on the world? Like the airplane analogy, (which I happen to be in right now flying from Barcelona to Geneva,) put on your own oxygen mask first. Don't worry about everyone else. Make the changes in you. When you change, you see the world differently. People will respond to you differently and your world will forever be changed.

CHAPTER 6

CLEANING OUT THE MIND

Scan the QR code or follow this link to watch the
video for this chapter. https://youtu.be/cDNtJ7F1jKM

Recently, I had my car detailed by one of those really good, come to your home, professionals who spends the whole day on your car. When he was done, he reported that the outside of my car was in pretty good shape, but the inside took him a lot more time. I thought about it and immediately knew the reason. I want my car to look good to others, so I'd wash and wax the outside every week. Not many people get in my car, so I'd put off the interior vacuuming as a monthly task. I justify this by explaining, no one besides the kids and myself get in the car anyway. I take the junk and trash out of my car each day, but the crumbs, dust and dirt stays put until my monthly vacuum. This behavior made me stop and think. Why am I more concerned with how my car looks on the outside for others than how it looks on the inside for my family and me? Shouldn't it be the other way around? I'd justify that it's easier to clean the outside of the car because I can drive through a quick car wash, but if I want the inside done, I have to spend more time, money or both. This situation made me question my intentions. Do I do what's easy and looks good from afar or do I want something better for my family and me?

Later that week I was at a yoga class and the instructor brought up a topic that was very similar. She said a student was telling her how exhausted she was from getting her house ready for company. She'd been vacuuming, dusting, washing bedding, dishes, laundry, yard work, etc. I started thinking, why do we let things go around us, but fix them up for others instead of for ourselves?

The teacher then posed an interesting question. What about the company between our ears? What kind of company are we for ourselves? Are we kind, sweet, empathetic, understanding and caring to ourselves like we would be to someone else or to a child or, do we treat ourselves poorly? I think if we are honest, most of us treat others better than we treat ourselves. Some of that poor treatment to ourselves comes from our own conscious thoughts, but most of it comes from negative programming in our subconscious that functions 24/7 without us even being aware. We might have had a parent that told us we always screw everything up. It seems bizarre, but in our adult lives we might manage to do just what that parent said. We seem to screw things up!

Maybe we had a parent that was not around and because of this we feel abandoned or unworthy. We prove these feelings to ourselves when a friend starts to get a bit distant. We might subconsciously think it's because we are not good enough or we said the wrong thing otherwise, they'd want to be around us more. We might turn to some type of self-soothing like food or alcohol to improve our mood or numb our feelings.

The good news is we can "clean" our minds! We can get rid of negative programs that derail us. Who has time for reprogramming the mind? Are we too busy to take care of us? Why? Maybe we don't feel worthy so we make ourselves busy by taking on too much so we can't take care of ourselves. It's the same reason I spend more time on the outside of the car instead of the inside. Maybe we get the house really clean for guests instead of for ourselves or our family. Maybe we don't value ourselves enough. Maybe we have to wait until our state becomes so urgent that we have to take care of us right that minute. Why wait to get to the point? Like we change the oil in our car to keep the engine running well, we should update our mind to live our best life.

I find that most clients I work with have some degree of negative self-worth. Realizing your own worth and divinity is a massive step forward in transforming your life. When you change how you see you, you change how you see the world. When you notice your beauty, inside and out, you see that mirrored back in everyone and everything around you. How do you realize your worth and divinity? You reprogram your subconscious mind of course.

Another reason some say they don't want to "clean" the mind is they've tried to change and it's hard; maybe impossible. They might think it's a slow, difficult process. That's because they've been going about it all wrong. The subconscious is easily programmable. It's easy to reprogram the mind. If you knew how easy it was to change, you'd grab your calendar and schedule it right now!

The first step in cleaning out the mind is figuring out what you want to be different and deciding if you are willing to change. It's not always easy to let go of old limiting beliefs. The subconscious will do it's best to keep you where you are at because that is your programming. Are you willing to let go of old habits and thoughts and take a good hard look at your life? Are you willing to take responsibility for where you are in your life? Are you willing to realize that you are creating your life from the inside out? Are you ready to stop blaming yourself or others and just reprogram your mind? If yes, congratulations on being so brave and keep reading!

Where are you now? Where would you rather be? Write these new goals down in a short, present tense, positive and emotionally meaningful statement like, "I am happy." Next find a method of subconscious change that you'd like to employ to "rewrite" your mind. Would you like to see the science behind the process we use? Check out these two videos, https://balancedyou.org/getting-ready-for-your-first-appointment/.

It's time to get out of your own way and let your system lead you to where you want to go. I had a full circle moment when it came to understanding the power of the mind. I was a headstrong kid with a mind of my own and zero respect for authority unless I felt they earned it. This did not go over well in my home. Like many, I was "forced" to act the way I was told. Early on, I started faking who I was and ignoring how I felt, because I perceived that I was not acceptable the way I was based on the responses I got when I shared my true thoughts and feeling.

This experience for the first 18 years of my life turned into a huge disconnect within myself and a lack of understanding of who I really was, how I felt, and what I really wanted. I was always trying instead of being. I commonly felt bad inside and did things to make up for those feeling like being ultrasuccessful in school, sports, music and work. Because I was very successful, I got lots of positive praise which helped ease some of the bad internal feelings.

The confusion was that this praise caused me to think I had good self-esteem. I'd notice, however, that when anyone would say or do something that I could somehow perceive as a negative, I'd feel crushed. Like I wanted to die type of crushed. Why did I feel so crushed? I didn't understand it. In typical Jenny fashion, I'd ignore these feeling and move on.

This internal disconnect made my marriage very hard. I started to project my internal feelings of "mad", "bad", "sad," blaming them on my husband because if he would just take out the trash when he said he would, then I would not feel so hurt. This realization is in hindsight of course. In the moment, I just thought my husband didn't care about me, didn't follow through, and must not love me, or he'd do what he said he'd do. All of that was untrue, but it was my conscious story to explain my painful feelings when he did anything that I could twist into blaming my own upset on him. The poor guy.

I started reading positive books and saying affirmations and again, trying to be something other than how I felt or what I was. I was not acknowledging what was really going on inside of me. I was trying to cover it up with positivity. Unfortunately, faking happiness to cover my pain did not help my internal feelings. I had a lot of health challenge throughout my life including chronic pain. Like any emotional feelings I had, I ignored the physical pain as much as I could and pushed though as much as possible. I was so out of touch with me.

I now know that my body really reacts to my surroundings and thoughts. I have to watch what I think, consciously and subconsciously, because if I don't, it can quickly turn into a tension headache, cold, pain etc. My system wants me to listen and If I don't, it forces me to! Tip one I learned is to watch my thoughts! This does not mean to ignore my thoughts or only think positive thoughts. This means be in touch with my thoughts while accepting my them and not suppressing or ignoring them.

In addition to *Healing Back Pain,* by Dr. John Sarno, I also highly recommend his books *The Mind Body Prescription* and *The Divided Mind.* These books help you with a deeper scientific understanding of how your body can cause your pain to keep you from being in touch with your subconscious emotions. If his words alone don't help your pain, he recommends a deeper process like ours at *Balanced You*.

Howard Stern said, "My life was filled with excruciating back and shoulder pain until I applied Dr. Sarno's principles, and in a matter of weeks my back pain disappeared. I never suffered a single symptom again...I owe Dr. Sarno my life." Now that's powerful!

Accepting ourselves and our thoughts does not mean we have to stay the way we are, and be proud of our character traits that we are not fond of, it means knowing ourselves, and loving and accepting ourselves. Then, if you don't like your thoughts, change your perception with the power of your subconscious mind. When you change your thoughts, you change your perception. When you see the world differently, you act differently and think differently. To change your state, you have to change your traits. The easiest way to change your traits is with subconscious change, which reprograms the subconscious thought patterns from your old programming to your new goals.

I've heard scientists say that 93% of our thoughts are the same every day. No wonder we get the same results in our lives and find it hard to change. If we are thinking the same thoughts, we really are repeating the past. Are we living in the future or the past? If we want to change the print-out of our life, we have to start with our mind and create a new future.

I was on vacation and met a man who was suffering with back pain. He said it was a herniated disk. He had been out of work on disability and was concerned about going back to work. He had a job with harder labor and his back was still not feeling quite healed. He was worried about his back and equally worried about losing his job if he took any more time off. Even sitting in a car was painful. I shared my story with him and told him that maybe his pain was not structural. He said that he really had hurt his back at work. I told him I believed him, but maybe it was healed but still feeling painful for emotional reasons. He looked at me a bit funny and then said, "that is kind of interesting because about a minute after my back got hurt at work, I got a phone call that my mother was critically ill, and that I needed to leave work and fly home. She passed away the next week." I told him that it was quite possible that the trauma of his mom's sudden sickness and passing could also be causing his pain. If that was the case, it would be easy to help him transform his pain.

Because I deal with pain and emotions all week with clients as well as my own pain of the past, I see daily how traumatic events cause physical pain for people. I also see how hidden subconscious emotion causes pain, too.

There are so many mothers with back pain. Many times, they think it's from carrying their baby, the diaper bag, or car seat. Could their back pain be caused by that? Yes! Have you ever tried to carry one of those baby car seat carriers with a baby in it? You've got to be a champion deadlifter to pick those things up! They are so awkward and heavy! Often I find the mother's back pain is coming from the stress of motherhood. How do I know? Because the moment we reprogram the subconscious mind to deal with the stress in their life, the pain stops.

I was seeing a pain client the other day and we had the discussion of how he will know when his pain stops. Will he feel the pain stop in his body and then his mind will acknowledge the pain is gone or, will he get rid of the pain thoughts in his mind and they will go away in his body? Do you feel something and then think it, or think it and then feel it? I think people experience it both ways. Either way, if you want to change any part of your life, you have to break the habitual cycle of the mind regarding that thought pattern.

Another client came in recently with chronic fatigue. It was so bad that she had to quit her job and she was barely functioning. She'd been to her doctor and he had run a battery of tests and found nothing. She and I did some muscle testing and found the fatigue was a reaction to a divorce she has decades earlier. She didn't think this made sense. She said she was over the divorce and it was not that bad to start with. She said the divorce was amicable and really the best thing for both of them.

The muscle test showed the divorce was traumatic to the subconscious mind. We did a stress release process to reprogram her subconscious perception of the divorce. She skipped out of my office, offering a tip, and hugged me profusely as she felt her energy coming back. She then yelled from the parking lot that her knees and back were no longer hurting, symptoms I had not even heard about from her when she came to see me.

I love the work I do. It's so simple, powerful and effective. I am not a healer. My clients heal themselves by reprogramming their own minds. When you change your mind, you change your chemistry and your biology. You are a different person who gets to live a different life. I love facilitating this process and watching the amazing results day in and day out. What a rewarding job!!!

What's the cause of your pain? What's the cause of your troubles? What's the cause of your unhappiness? What's the cause of the things that are going on in your life that you don't like? Maybe these things have a message for you? If there was a message, what is it? Close your eyes and think about it. What needs to change in your life. What can you learn? Be still for a bit and listen. What answer comes to you?

CHAPTER 7

OVERCOMING CHRONIC PAIN

Scan the QR code or follow this link to watch the video
for this chapter. https://youtu.be/M1yWQYlCEuM

I used to think my mind and body were separate. Maybe because I grew up in the US where we learn that if our body hurts, we should go to the doctor. The doctor asks what's wrong with our body and attempts to fix our body. The doctor typically asks if we were in an accident, a sports injury, or if the condition runs in our family. The doctor can order blood tests, x-rays, prescriptions, surgery, recommend physical therapy, etc. but what about the mind? Does the mind have anything to do with this equation?

I suffered with endometriosis for 20+ years. While trying to resolve that issue, I was never asked by a doctor what was going on in my life emotionally. To make a long story short, I finally had surgery to help the endometriosis pain. The surgery didn't help so, at 35 years old, I decided to have a full hysterectomy. Luckily the surgery fixed the pain, but the pain came back in another form. The body really is a perfect feedback machine and I clearly was not getting the message. My wise system was again attempting to talk to me! First it was talking to me though chronic infections I was having after the surgery for about 18 months followed by a diagnosis of interstitial cystitis which is a condition that feels like a bladder infection, but the tests show no infection. It's terrible pain, so much so that some people have their bladder removed and pee into a bag for the rest of their lives to stop the pain.

At age 37, I broke my back. I could not catch a "break" with my health, pun intended. At least with endometriosis, the pain was only brutal during my menstrual cycle. During my endometriosis years, I lived my life 3 weeks per month active and 1 week per month curled up in a ball crying or taking 30 ibuprofen per day. As my back healed the pain increased. The back pain turned into burning pain 24/7 for years. So, what did I do? First, I tried all the eastern medicine ideas I knew of, but after years of trying and not even being able to sit in a chair, I gave in and had major surgery. I was hopeful that the surgery would get rid of my pain. I was not so lucky this time around. Rods, screws and a synthetic disc later, the burning pain continued plus I had a lot of surgery healing to do.

My body was trying to talk to me and I was NOT LISTENING. I later learned that the pain I was feeling in my body was a response to the pain in my mind. I didn't realize this was going on. If someone would have told me my emotions were affecting my body, I would have told them they were crazy, and my life was great. I learned very well how to hide my own emotional pain, even from myself. It took quite a bit of digging before the truth came out of me. The real issues came out and the pain stopped. What a blessed day that was.

Next time you have an ache, pain, or even if you have something chronic, think of my story and ask yourself, what could be causing your pain? Close your eyes. What surprising thing pops into your mind that you were not expecting. That thing might just be the key to unlocking your best life.

When pain pops up for me today, I know why it's there. It's there to block a subconscious emotion. Now, to get over pain, I'd just ask myself what is going on emotionally. What emotion am I trying to hide from myself? What emotion do I not want to feel or deal with? Then I allow the emotion to surface and I'd kindly and gently deal with it and the pain disappears. This was fascinating! How had I never heard of this method of pain relief before?

If you think you have no emotional stuff going on, I know how you feel. I thought that, too. The emotional stuff is hiding out in the subconscious mind. The subconscious is just that, subconscious. Out of our awareness. If you want to know what's going on in the subconscious, listen to the chatter in your head when you are sitting at a traffic light. What limiting beliefs do you hear?

Maybe you are totally aware of your emotions. Then why are you still in pain? Most likely you are still in pain because you have not made the connection between pain and the emotional issues. Your pain is there to keep you from feeling your emotions. Connect those two dots, really believe it, address the blocked subconscious emotion if you can find it, and the pain should vanish.

A certain little man in my family hates this method. If he calls me from school saying he is "sick" and needs to come home, I help him discover the subconscious emotion that his body is blocking, causing him to feel sick. Then I help him to transform his perception, and he feels better. Dang it, no more getting out of school with this mom!

Would you consider believing this method of pain relief? Even if the doctor says your pain is physical? Remember Dr. Sarno and his 90% success rate with chronic pain patients? Dr. Sarno explains that almost all pain is caused by subconscious, he calls it unconscious, blocking emotions. He believes this because once he helps his clients make the connections between their emotions and their physical pain, plus additional resources like ours if needed, most all of them become pain free. That is amazing! I don't know any other doctor with those types of results! These are chronic pain patients who have probably tried countless methods to get over their pain before dealing with their mind. Powerful!

What about my MRI's or x-rays? Dr. Sarno explains that he can look at two images of two different people with the same diagnosis, say "bulging disks." One can have severe chronic pain and one can be pain free. If the pain is physical due to the bulging disks, how could it hurt one person and not another? Dr. Sarno explains what's really going on is ischemia. Ischemia is lack of blood flow which causes oxygen deprivation and pain to muscles, nerves, joints or tendons. Luckily, no damage is being done, it just hurts wherever there is a lack of blood flow. What does he recommend? He recommends that you tell yourself you are hurting not because you have bulging discs, but because you have ischemia caused by your emotions. Then look into your emotions.

He also recommends that as soon as you make this connection and your pain stops, to go back to doing the things you've been avoiding, like exercise. He says to stop thinking you'll hurt yourself worse because of this supposed physical issue. Get away from fear which makes your pain worse.

Let's get one thing very clear. I am not a doctor, nor do I have any medical degrees. I have learned from my own chronic pain and recovery as well as training within various modalities of subconscious change. I also studied the work of Dr. John Sarno, Dr. Warren Jacobs, Touch for Health and PSYCH-K®.

What I practice is a method of reprogramming the mind. This process is used when the realization of the pain being caused by emotions is not quite enough to stop the pain or when you want to program a goal or perception change into your subconscious mind. About 20% of people will be pain free just from making the connection to their subconscious emotional pain being the cause of their physical pain. An ah-ha moment can clear the pain. The other

80% of people will need a bit more clearing of the subconscious mind to get to that place of pain free, and that's okay.

I DO want you to see a doctor if you have pain. Sometimes there is something serious going on that you need a medical doctor for. If the situation is not life threatening and you'd like to try your hand at curing your own pain, we at *Balanced You* would love to assist you in that process.

Maybe you are like me and have tried EVERYTHING out there for pain relief and nothing has worked. Maybe you've seen more doctors than you can count. Maybe this is the solution you've been praying for.

Download our no-cost *A Pain Free Life* workbook to help you find more clarity on where you pain may be coming from, https://transformmypain.com/.

If you are like me, I was desperate for answers. I wanted my life back. I wanted to go out and have fun again. I didn't want my decisions to hinge on my pain level. I wanted to have a social life again. I wanted to exercise. I wanted to spend time with my friends. Heck, I just wanted to sit in a chair. Was that too much to ask?

Are you ready to change your pain? Schedule a 30-minute complimentary *Balanced You* intro call with us so we can find out what's working for you, what's not and what you want to be different in your life. Then we can decide if we have a resource that can help you. Schedule your no-cost intro call at https://balancedyou.org/.

Disclaimer: As with any method Eastern or Western, results with *Balanced You* are not guaranteed.

Chapter 8

What DO You Want?

Scan the QR code or follow this link to watch the video for this chapter. https://youtu.be/nohyjJHKXj4

I can't tell you how many times clients come to my office and tell me how awful their lives are. I feel so bad for them. I get it. I've been there. BUT the only thing that matters in our process is changing your life. To change your life, you have to know what you want. Ask yourself, what do you want different in your life? Your subconscious speaks in sensory language. If your subconscious mind can't understand your goal, it can't help you create that realty. So describe the goal to your subconscious mind. Imagine if you had already accomplished your goal, what would sound different, feel different, smell different, look different, and maybe even taste different in your life? Grab a journal and write your goals and describe them like you already had accomplished them in sensory language. Make sure that after you describe the goal in sensory language that you ask yourself, now that you know how this goal will turn out, do you really want this goal?

Sometimes we find that there is a price to be paid for our goal and you actually don't want it. No problem, change your goal and re-write what it looks, sounds, and feels like with your new goal. Really feel it in your body. Then, if you are positive that you want that goal to become your new reality, reach out to us so we can help you with a simple, powerful, and effective process to program your subconscious mind to accomplish all your goals.

Your life is supposed to feel great and joyful. For me, the secret to feeling great was all about discovering what was hiding out in my subconscious mind and reprogramming the parts that were not serving me. The subconscious controls how we feel 95-99% of the time, so if we are not feeling great, I believe the best place to start is the subconscious mind. The subconscious controls our biology and our chemistry. Let's start there. What a powerful place to start!

For me, I had a lot of work to do to get back to feeling good, even great. First, I needed to clear out my negative subconscious beliefs as well as flushing out traumas and dramas that were still disrupting my system. The subconscious is timeless, so you may find a trauma 30 years ago is just as traumatic today in the subconscious. When we walk around traumatized, we experience negative side effects that cause us unhappiness, pain and even addictions to try to soothe the subconscious pain. When we release those traumas and dramas, we feel a huge weight lifted. Some of my clients tell me they feel like the shackles were released and they never even knew they were wearing them until they felt the freedom of being unshackled. What a powerful testimony!

Another key for me to overcoming my pain was being true to myself and following my passion. I was doing a job that was not my passion because I was making big money and loved the lifestyle. I didn't know what other job I could do and make as much money and still work from home juggling my 4 kids. I told myself to just suck it up, but after 13 years I could not do a job I was not loving anymore. I had to figure out what I was passionate about. From Dr. Jacobs I learned that with muscle testing, we can tap into our deep inner knowing and find the answers that seem to be evading us. I found that my purpose was to help others live their purpose and I do that by helping them get rid of the limiting beliefs that hold them back, and keep them trapped in physical or emotional pain and not living their potential. I help them remove the shackles of their own minds, so they can fill the measure of their creation. What an awesome calling I have!

While dealing with my subconscious, I found that I was programmed with all sorts of limiting beliefs about my health, self-esteem, relationships, prosperity, grief, loss, personal power, the list goes on and on. I needed to get my core beliefs in alignment. If my subconscious believes that I love myself and that I hate myself, that is confusion in my system and it feels like discord, dissonance, depression and an exhausting tug of war which I believe added to my physical pain.

I also had to forgive myself and others, and be responsible for my own life instead of blaming others. I had to flush out all trauma through my entire life, past, present, and fears of the future. After all this was straight, which sounds like a lot but was really quite pleasurable to release, I felt physical, mental, and spiritual joy. It was always in me, it was just covered up by many layers of limiting beliefs that kept me from my highest self, purpose, and expression. What a relief to get out from under all of that!

The subconscious is 1 million times more powerful than the conscious mind. If it's pulling you down, it's nearly impossible to fight. Free yourself with the power of reprogramming the subconscious mind. Imagine it like someone who is losing their vision and has to hold a piece of paper either further away or closer to be able to see it. What if you said, "sorry, you have to see it right where I choose to hold it?" They might be able to strain and see it for a minute, but they probably could not read a book like that. Put that paper at the right distance for them and they can easily decipher the words. With mindfulness, the conscious mind can try to feel how you want to feel, but the moment you stop trying to be mindful because your focus turns to something else, that mindful feeling is overpowered by a subconscious program.

I feel incredibly blessed to have found this subconscious change process. With it I have gotten rid of my physical pain which was so bad I could not even sit down for years. With this subconscious power I fixed my relationships so that they are continuing and thriving instead of withering and dying. It's allowed me to feel a joy I've never felt before. Life IS supposed to feel good and I'm so glad to finally feel it!

When I programmed my mind, my current life of pain and struggle turned into a whole new beautiful life. The funny thing was that nothing actually changed in my life but, it felt like everything changed because I saw myself and everyone else differently. Because I saw everything differently, I acted differently. When I acted differently, others felt and acted differently too. Immediately my life was transformed.

Believing in something causes a chemical and biological effect which is why changing subconscious beliefs is such a powerful way to change. These beliefs change biology as Dr. Bruce Lipton, cellular biologist explains in his book, *The Biology of Belief.*

I watched a video of a man who lost his finger. The doctor gave him "finger regrowth powder" and guess what happened? Yes, his finger grew back! http://bit.ly/FingerRegrowth. He believed it would and it did! That is the power of the mind! "Whatever the mind can conceive and believe, it can achieve." -Napoleon Hill.

What gives a person a sense of satisfaction? I've seen myself and others looking outside of themselves for satisfaction. According to Eckhart Tolle in his book *A New Earth*, "only the truth of who you are can set you free." Does freedom equal satisfaction? In my mind, they are pretty close. How do you know who you are? Is there something you are meant to be and do? There are lots of methods for finding your way.

Listening to your superconscious, the highest power you believe in, is the best way I've found. My superconscious is God and when I am open to asking Him questions and I listen for the answer, He speaks to me. The more I practice, the easier it is for me to hear His voice.

If you are open to listening to answers, you will hear or feel or sense them. The answers you "hear" won't always be what you want, but if you follow your superconscious, which I know as God, you are sure to find greater joy than if you consciously push your way through life making choices without guidance from above. Listening to your superconscious will get you to the right place. Like animal migration found in all major animal groups, including birds, mammals, fish, reptiles, amphibians, insects, and crustaceans, animals go where they are meant to go for a better life, more food, better mating and birthing conditions, and survival of their species. Also, for their enjoyment I'd add.

The physical body is the "loudest" and most noticeable portion of our system for most people. When we are hungry, tired, thirsty we act. When was the last time you felt something in your spirit and jumped to quench that spiritual thirst as quick as you reach for food when you are hungry?

Superconscious or spiritual guidance is typically more of a whisper and takes time and practice to learn to tune into. Because of this, we tend to push it to the bottom of the to-do list or maybe never listen at all. The body, mind and spirit are one. When one portion of ourselves is off, it throws the rest of the system off. Then we might feel bad, mad, sad, depressed, sick, tired, fatigued, pain and can't figure out why. We head to the doctor to treat our symptom instead of the root of the problem.

The real problem is we didn't "fly south for the winter." We are living the wrong season, in the wrong climate and are suffering. I believe the "pain" we feel is just our system trying to get our attention. Trying to get us back on track. Yes, a pill from the doctor might numb the pain for a season, but getting your whole self on track is a much better way for ultimate health and wellbeing, satisfaction and freedom. YOU are incharge of your life. What do you want different? You have the power to change it all.

Chapter 9

Living the Good Life

Scan the QR code or follow this link to watch the video for this chapter. https://youtu.be/nohyjJHKXj4

I'm excited to share that you really can live the life of your dreams. I know this because I've done it by reprogramming my mind. I used to suffer from "mad, bad, sad, sick and in pain syndrome." I'd put on a happy face and pretend I was doing great. I would ask myself why I felt so miserable on the inside, but I could not figure it out. I blamed my bad feelings on others. If my husband would just…if my kids would just…if my clients would just…and the list went on and on. I didn't want to blame these feelings on myself.

After I programmed my own mind, all my problems vanished. My physical and emotional pain went away, my marriage did a 180, my grief and loss was gone, my life became full of joy, happiness and peace. I also started eating better, stopped stress eating, and my weight battles left me. I go in depth into that in my book, *101 Things I Wish I Knew Before I Fed My Children*. I had been trying to create a happy life consciously, but it would not happen for me. It was equivalent to yelling at my computer when I wanted to install a new program. No matter how loud I yelled, it just didn't change the programming on my computer.

I tried looking further into myself and my life to find the negative patterns and stop them, but it felt like an ant trying to walk up an avalanche. I could not consciously compete with the power of my programming. It seemed impossible to change no matter how hard I tried. Once I programmed my subconscious mind, all the trying was gone and there was only *being*. What a sweet relief.

How do you find Balance? "Balance my darling, balance is not letting anybody love you less than you love yourself. That's what balance is." That's one of my favorite lines from the movie, Eat. Pray. Love. Loving yourself is definitely a key to finding balance.

It's true, when you love yourself, and see your greatness, you are only comfortable around people who treat you the way you feel about yourself. That could also explain why people who were raised in an abusive home tend to find abusive relationships. It's not what they want, but it's what they feel comfortable around because of how they feel about themselves. Their subconscious attracts those type of people to them.

I love photos of balancing rocks. There is not one right way to balance. We are all different and different things help us to feel balanced. I feel more balanced when I take time for myself. If I fill my internal bank account, I have "money" to spend. If I'm always spending and not "refilling my bank account," I can no longer spend for myself, or for others. If I run a deficit, it takes even longer to break even or get ahead because of the "insufficient funds fees" that put me even further behind. The insufficient funds can be things like getting sick because I've worn myself down so much, not getting enough sleep, or working my brain for too long with no breaks. One thing that helps me feel balanced the most is being outside in my garden. I love growing my own food and flowers and just enjoying nature. I also feel balanced when I work a reasonable number of hours instead of working all the time. I love to go for walks around my neighborhood with my adorable little doggie, Sammie. I feel balance when I spend quality time with my husband and enjoy our bond. It really feels like a great recharge for me.

Subconsciously, the very best way I find balance is to change my perception. Some of my perceptions were not what I wanted them to be. How I was seeing myself and others was causing me pain. The story I was telling myself was not true. My story was my conscious mind making up the best narrative it could to protect my underlying negative limiting beliefs that I could not see. The most transformative thing I've changed in my perception is my self-esteem. I've found that when you love yourself, everything else changes. When you love yourself, you mirror love instead of fear, and like a mirror, that love comes right back. My definition of balance is close to the movie quote. Balance is loving yourself so much that everyone and everything you attract is love. Now that's a beautiful life!

"You are already perfect, flawless in every way. Some of you don't know that, you were never told that perfection already exists within you.

What's gotten in the way are all these limiting beliefs (not good enough, smart enough, etc.) that are layered and layered and layered over that.

The goal is not to add to you. How can perfection be added to?

It's to remove those things that get in the way.

Take away that which is untrue.

Take away false beliefs and perspectives.

Once you see yourself as perfect, your body, your performance, life and health will mirror that.

Our reality is designed to mirror back to us what we think of it. If we see ourselves as big, we'll have a big experience of life. When we see ourselves as small, we have a small existence.

We live in a dynamic reality that is not fixed, but mirrors what is believed about it.

To change your life, you'll need to change your beliefs."
-Limitless Athlete Explained by Daniel Rechnitzer

Do you think you are perfect? Most would say NO! Why not? Maybe it's because we have limiting beliefs. Maybe we are afraid of being prideful or letting our ego take over. Thinking we are less than affects how we feel mentally, physically and spiritually. What keeps you from happiness, health and wellness in your body, mind, and spirit are your beliefs. Your beliefs affect your biology. Change your perception and you change your biology. Change your biology and you change your life.

Have you ever tried to change your perception? Trying to change a belief is not that easy to do. At least not with the conscious mind. That is where the secret lies. You've got to change your subconscious beliefs if you want to change your life.

Again, ask yourself, where you are now and where would you rather be? Which belief programs would you like to be running in your subconscious? The next step is to find a system to program those beliefs into your subconscious, so they become your new automatic. Your new knee jerk reaction could be happiness, success, peace, health and calm instead of stress, anxiety, dis-ease, financial burdens, and pain.

You are only hours away from a whole new life. Hard to believe, right? Especially when people struggle with things for their whole life. I've seen firsthand the success of subconscious change with myself and my clients. You can let go of things in minutes that you've been holding on to for decades!

I've guided clients quickly through overcoming all types of physical pain and dis-ease, depression, anxiety, weight gain/loss, traumatic situations in their lives, phobias, death, relationship issues, business failures and more. The answers for you lie in your subconscious mind. With a neuromuscular testing system, we walk you through a process to change your neural pathways which changes your perception and changes your reality.

I'd love to share this process with you. When you think about your life, what's the undercurrent? Is it joy, peace and pleasure or something less desirable? One thing I've really enjoyed about getting older is learning things like, life is what I make it. I always thought it was more black and white when I was young. Something bad happened, so I'd be mad or upset. Something good happened, so I'd be happy. I've learned I can feel joy, calm, and gratitude at any time. Not just when life is going great.

You are Divine, you are beautiful, you are magnificent. Yes, You! You are a masterpiece of co-creation between you and Creation itself. Everything that you are is in perfection. If it doesn't look perfect or feel perfect, then it is leading to something more perfect. You, my dear one, are an individualized expression of the Universe, whole and complete. There is nothing wrong with you and you are not broken. You have a body, you have a life, but neither of those things define, they are only part of the package, the outer coverings for the Soul that you are.

We are here to discover the deeper parts of ourselves, those that are indeed perfect. We are here to connect with and express our Essence. Our essence is the truth of who we are and who we are becoming, way beyond the physical reality of life on this planet we call Earth. Our Essence can be discovered as we let go of limiting thoughts, as we release all the old stories and beliefs we've collectively had for millennia; those of unworthiness, separation, not being good enough, or loved enough.

It's time to STOP the nonsense of false beliefs. It's time to step into your glory and embrace the truth of you! It's already there, like the David that Michelangelo revealed as he chipped away at the marble block. Imagine that you, and all of your experiences, are a beautiful block of marble and that the discovery and revelation of your essence is like chipping away all that does not represent the true you.

Some of the chips will be removing unworthiness, beliefs of not being loved or not being 'enough'. You know your beliefs, are you ready to let them go, so you can step into a true sense of being?

We are being called into oneness, into wholeness. The only way there is to let go of and transcend the false. Let it go! Come into a conscious awareness, step onto a conscious journey of letting go. You might be asked to let go of fear or anger, guilt or blame. You will most definitely be asked to release all the shame that hides out in the darkness. Shed the fears, shed the limits and step into your Divine!

The above content is adapted for this book from Rev. Aliza Bloom Robinson. http://www.divine-awakening.org/you-are-divine/.

Powerful, right? I get excited reading her words, but one million times more powerful than words is your subconscious programming. Imagine how you would feel if those words from Rev. Robinson were programmed into your subconscious mind. Imagine if those words were your new automatic? You are only one step away from feeling divine every minute of every hour of every day. That's the power of reprogramming the subconscious mind.

On my wall hangs a picture entitled Influence. It says, "The positive action of one person reverberates endlessly throughout humanity." You can be the change in their world. You are the change in this world. Let your light shine.

Why is it important for us to accept our own divinity? *"Accept your own divinity. Everything is a manifestation of God. When you know that, the power that is life is inside you, you accept your own divinity, and yet you are humble, because you see that the same divinity in everyone else."* – Miguel Ruiz

How differently would we treat others if we saw our divinity and theirs all the time? Instead of getting caught up in disagreements or contention or being right, we just love each other.

"Take the road of seeing the face of God in everyone you encounter. Look for something to appreciate in others and be willing to communicate it to them and anyone who's willing to listen. When you see this quality in others, you'll soon begin

to realize that this potential is available to all of humanity." – Wayne W. Dyer

This includes you. Recognizing genius in yourself is an integral part of the dynamic. As Dr. David Hawkins tells us in Power vs. Force: *"Until one acknowledges the genius within oneself, one will have great difficulty recognizing it in others."*

Does your purpose really matter? Do you really have a divine mission to fulfill? I have to agree with Eckhart Tolle, *"You are here to enable the divine purpose of the Universe to unfold. That is how important you are!"*

I believe we are here for a reason with a mission to fulfill. I believe in you and your divinity and also in your divine purpose. I believe that getting your limiting subconscious beliefs out of the way, allows you to live your purpose and fill the measure of your divinity.

If you don't know what your divine purpose is, we at Balanced You, have a method to help you find it. You have an inner knowing that we can help you tap into and find the answers you are searching to find. Tapping into your inner knowing is not woo-woo. It's science. Get in touch with you at a deeper level. Put the powerhouse of the subconscious mind to work for you to help you feel your divinity and live your purpose.

It's freeing to get the conscious mind out of the way and operate at a deeper more spiritual level. The conscious mind is more of a narrator, telling the story of your life. This narration comes from your lens of beliefs. The lens you are looking through, colors how you see and tell your own story. Would you like to change the lens? Would you like to change the story of you? Would you like to experience the divine you and live your divine purpose? Doing so brings peace, joy, love, happiness, contentment and fulfillment into your life. Ready for more of that?

Can we actually change our state of being? Can we change our state so much that it changes our traits? According to epigenetics we can. Epigenetics is *"the study of changes in organisms caused by modification of gene expression rather than alteration of the genetic code itself."* http://bit.ly/ epigenetics4change.

Changing how your system reads the gene instead of changing the gene. That's power! When your system reads the gene differently, it produces different results. The gene is a blueprint and the cell decides when and how to execute what is on the blueprint by what it perceives. The cell can also rewrite the gene. This is exciting news as we used to think our genes controlled us. We control our genes. According to cellular biologists like Bruce Lipton PhD, it does not matter what's in our family history, it matters how we express our blueprint based on our beliefs and perceptions. This puts the power back in our court. I love this!

A client of mine insisted I get the book, *Dying to be Me* by Anita Moorjani. Wowzers! What a powerful story. I won't tell you too much of the story because I'm hoping you get the book too, but I will share a few things. Anita had a pretty hard life, but she was mostly hard on herself because of how she perceived herself and the world around her. She was a worrier and an anxious type of person with lots of reasons to be that way based on her upbringing. Anita later got cancer and was dying. In the hospital in a coma, she had a near death experience that changed everything.

What changed the most was Anita's perception of herself, of the world, of her experiences and of others. Her perception changed so much that she was healed. She realized that for her, the cancer was just her fear and non-acceptance coming to life. Her near death experience got rid of her fear. She explains her life before was like wandering in a huge dark warehouse, with only a flashlight, and then one day someone turned on the light and it all made sense. A whole new perspective. Anita promotes the unconditional love she felt during this near death experience and how everything made sense when she "saw" or really "felt" the big picture. She shares how divine we are and if we would focus on that and truly understand that, our lives will be so much happier and healthier.

I thought about my own injury, breaking my back in 2013, and how it was truly getting to know and understand myself and my purpose that healed me. ALL the other methods of Eastern and Western healing I tried for years to get rid of my pain had zero effect. Then one day, I met Dr. Warren Jacobs, an MD turned emotional kinesiologist. He says, "In my work, in my experience- the greatest block to health I find is lack of self-acceptance." Dr. Jacobs helped me get to know and accept myself to heal myself. What an amazing miracle for me! After reading Anita's book and thinking about my own story, I thought that my experience was not too different from Anita's. She was *Dying to be Me* and I was *Breaking to be Me*. Hence my book title. Thank you, Anita!

Another huge fan of this school of thought is Louise Hay. She also healed herself of cancer and other ailments by changing her perception. Our perception is based on the programming of our subconscious minds which happened to us while growing up and was complete by around age 7 years old. Most of us update our technology frequently, but do we update our subconscious programming so that it serves us? My wish for you is that you will not have to die or break, but can learn from the lessons we have learned. To love and accept yourself and others unconditionally, that is the greatest love and gift of all.

You have the power to turn your life into anything you choose. I hope you will choose joy, happiness, peace, love, forgiveness, compassion, charity, health, spirituality, prosperity, and to follow your dreams. The decision is yours. Which path will you choose?

For more info on programming the subconscious mind, please visit our website. You may also schedule a 30-minute complimentary Balanced You Intro call session with us at https://balancedyou.org/. This process works in person and remotely as we can walk you through the process online.

Here is to your health and happiness, body, mind, and spirit.

Client Testimonials:

"Thank you to Balanced You for helping my son get over 20 years of stomach, back, and foot pain. Thank you for assisting my mom to get out of the hospital and start eating again and thank you for helping me get over my knee pain. Our family is so grateful for Balanced You and that we learned how the power of our minds can change our lives and our health."-Rosa

"I used to hold on to so much stress. Stress at work with clients, stress at home with the family, and stress about being a good provider for my family. I can confidently say that the balancing techniques at Balanced You will absolutely make a positive difference in your life. Answer two questions: Are you stressed today? Would you like it to be different tomorrow? If your answer to both of these questions is YES, then you really need to talk to one of the facilitators at Balanced You. I am thankful to know her and have experienced her company's results first-hand. Highly recommended A+."-Andrew

"Jenny - the pain in my body is 98% better since I saw you last. What you do for me and others is just amazing. I can't wait to come and do some more work with you. You are such a blessing to me. Thanks," -Jeanette

"Hi Jenny, I still have the elated feeling of insight that I left your office with. It's like you put jumper cables on me and got me re-started!! And, amazingly, not only did the self-worth belief shift but also I have a clear insight as to when, how and where the faulty belief started, and what the influences were on my relationships. Thank you so much!!! I'm so proud of the work!! It's truly unbelievable!!"-Jill

"I can't say enough good about Jenny and Balanced You. There are many things I'd like to change about myself. Jenny makes it so easy and I can feel that this is so much more than a "job" for her. She genuinely loves to help people feel better about themselves and the life they live. I'm so thankful for the healing she's helped me do and that I am able to live the life I've always dreamed of living. Thank you Jenny!" -Hanna

"Thank you Jenny for helping me work through issues I've carried since 5th grade. It's so good to finally be able to let go of them in my 60's. I feel so much lighter in spirit and happier. I will highly recommend you for helping people work through things that hold them back from a more fulfilled life." -Sandy

"Throughout life we grab hold of limiting beliefs that prevent us from living Extraordinary lives. I believe some of these thought patterns can be changed through book reading and listening to audio books. But the beliefs that have been lodged deep in the depths of our minds need an extra touch, a human touch. Jenny Harkleroad from Balanced You offers that personal touch, that extra nudge to break free from the beliefs that hold you back." -Orlando

"Balancing has made a huge difference for me. At first I didn't want to try it but after the very first session I saw a huge difference. It was impossible to deny. And it just kept getting progressively better from there. I went from severely depressed to at peace with life. I now know I have the power to change anything in my life." -Brooklynn 14 years old.

"Jenny is amazing and has helped me change and heal physically, mentally and emotionally. I would recommend her to anyone who wants to make some positive changes in their life." -Kristine

"After our appointment, I definitely felt different (altered)

*and if it is possible to feel my neurons rewiring, then that was the sensation I was having for a few hours after our balance session. The next day, after not much sleep, I had a morning class and later rehearsal, but instead of feeling drained or tired, I felt great. Still feeling calm even when a super annoying event happened during rehearsal. Overall, I sense more energy instead of feeling drained or weak. Yesterday, I received the notice for the end of my current work contract. I didn't experience any negative reaction to the news. Instead I know I need to address money issues and the big question of what work I should be doing with my life. Topics for our next meeting." Thank you!»-*Helena

*"I have to admit, I was a skeptic at first. I don't often believe things I haven't disseminated 1,000 different ways, countered with a hundred different arguments. After working with Jenny for several months though, the results are undeniable. I have released limiting beliefs, and have replaced them with more positive, life enhancing beliefs. When we work together, I feel an immediate, affirmative shift that lasts. I've noticed that in general I feel lighter, happier and freer than I have in many years. Jenny is honest, understanding, approachable, nonjudgmental, and kind — qualities that help facilitate me tapping into answers that already exist within myself. I am still working with Jenny, and will continue to do so, as I feel the work is immensely beneficial to my personal well-being, my marriage, and my relationship with my daughter."-*Kelli

*"I was having a hay fever type allergic reaction. Jenny said she could try to help me. My eyes were bloodshot and I could not even open them they were burning so bad. My nasal cavity was also hurting. Jenny did a balance with me and 10 minutes later my eyes were open, the bloodshot color turned to white and I felt no pain or burning or itching in my eyes or nose. Wow! Typically I'd have to sleep off this reaction and the next day my eyes would still be bothering me. Amazing!"-*Dusty

"After the balance session with Jenny, I am no longer feeling

guilty if I take some time to read quietly or just take time for myself. That is big for me. I have never been willing to be nice to myself that way. I am also able to make decisions much more easily than I ever have before. My stuffy nose and sneezing are also much better! I had been taking antihistamines for years but was able to stop taking them after we did a balance for my stuffy nose and sneezing. Thank you!"-Deanna

"Since seeing you for a balance I'm having less stomach issues. Things also seem better with my x. I'm now able to see him in a loving way. Thank you!" -Erin

"I am enjoying more time taking my kids out for treats (which I was struggling with in the past before the balance session as I only wanted my kids to eat healthy 100% of the time and it was turning into a real struggle.) I took the girls to a salad restaurant and then for some gelato. We had so much relaxed time together and I just loved it! They were all smiles and looking forward to more special times together. Me too! I no longer dread that inner battle I had been having with myself. I am also taking a parenting course online and it is easier for me to be consistent when going through the material, to not guilt myself about not finishing when I set out to, but to just enjoy what I have learned so far. Thank you so much for helping me to balance myself and enjoy my life and my family more."-Alicia

"Balanced You is amazing! I've done EVERYTHING that I could get my hands on for the past 30 years and had reached a dead end. Jenny had the key and she helped me to unlock that step. Since then my life has done a 360. I'm no longer afraid of taking risks because of feelings of unworthiness and rejection. Thanks to Balanced You for helping me change, I am now able to move forward without fear and landed a great job! Thank you from the bottom of my subconscious mind."-Theresa

"Before our session I was crying almost daily. One day after *our balance session I stopped crying and started processing my emotions instead. I feel more honor and respect for my parents and appreciate their advice. The tension with them is gone. I feel tangibly different and lighter. I feel in control of my words and I'm complementing and encouraging others more. I feel very productive. I can think and heal and process."* -Olivia, 17 years old.

"I recently completed the Balanced You Ultimate Success Program. The benefits I got from the program are: I am able to stay focused at work without letting distractions upset me or stress me out. I am engaging better with the colleagues that report to me and have been able to keep them focused at work as well. I have increased my production at work and am able to relax more at home and not stress about work on the weekends. I am more confident at work and feel very proud of my accomplishments. I am amazed at how this process made such a difference for me. I highly recommend Jenny and the Balanced You facilitators and their programs. It was a joy to go thru the Ultimate Success program and it really does work!" -Barb (Banking)

"I am more confident, bold, centered, fearless, I hit top salesperson of the quarter with a new deal I closed this week. I'm more consistent, it's easier to connect with others, things no longer get to me that used to bother me. I'm more light hearted and always laughing. I thank my boss everyday day for investing in me as one of the leaders on her team. I'm excited for even more mind reprogramming. The sky's the limit!" -Claudia, (Insurance Sales)

VIDEO TESTIMONIALS:

Traumatic Brain Injury symptom and emotional trauma testimonial:
http://bit.ly/DebbraSweetTestimonial.

Back Pain Relief testimonial:
http://bit.ly/MikeZerbatoTestimonial.

Business Success:
http://bit.ly/KaraBusinessTestimonial.

IBS Symptoms and more about Balanced You:
http://bit.ly/BalancedYouInfo.

Radio Show Guest Testimonial:
http://bit.ly/RadioShowTestimonial.

Interview with Jenny by Karin Bradshaw about chronic pain:
http://bit.ly/ApainFreeLife.

The Science of Change and the Art of Alignment by Jenny on the
Play to Win Podcast:
http://bit.ly/ChangeAndAlignment.

Video clip of Jenny speaking to a business group:
http://bit.ly/JennySpeakingBusiness.

Would you like Jenny to speak to your group?
https://balancedyou.org/about-psych-k/speaking/.

Find more videos by Jenny on YouTube: Balanced You

35860383R00060

Made in the USA
Middletown, DE
10 February 2019